MW00669238

Faith 365 Bucket Journal for Latter-day Saints
Your Daily TALK with God

ISBN:
Publisher: My Bucket Journals. LLC
PO Box 310, Hutto, Texas 78634

Disclaimer
The information in this book is based on the author's opinion, knowledge and experience. The publisher and the author will not be held liable for the use or misuse of the information contained herein.

Disclosure
This book may contain affiliate links. If you click through an affiliate link to a third-party website and make a purchase, the author may receive a small commission.

Cover photo ©DepositPhotos

The Faith 365 Bucket Journal, Latter-day Saint Edition gives you a place to have a daily TALK with God through prayer and record your impressions before and after. TALK stands for thankfulness, ask, let go, and keeping God in your day.

How to Use Your Faith 365 Bucket Journal for Latter-day Saints

We've provided 365 daily KJV scripture verses, hymn book excerpts, and general conference talk references to inspire your faith, encourage your service and give you comfort in trials.

The daily pages are not dated so that you can start your Faith 365 Bucket Journal at any time.

- Expressing gratitude to God is an integral part of prayer. Identify three things you are **Thankful** for each day, then mention these blessings in your prayer as you speak with God.

- We are commanded to **Ask** with sincerity of heart; blessings will come to us when we ask in faith (James 1:5)

  - We may need to ask for forgiveness for ourselves and also ask for our daily needs.
  - We may need to ask God to help with a specific challenge today.
  - We may want to ask God to bless certain people in our prayers today.

- There is space to note your worries and the things that may be bothering you; that you can't control. When you **Let** go and let God handle it, you can find peace.

- After your prayers, **Keep** God top of mind throughout the day and keep communicating with God throughout the day. You can do this by looking for blessings, big and small, and recognizing opportunities to help others.

Do you find that you can go for days or weeks, letting life happen to you? What you intend to attract often shows up in the most unexpected ways. Prayer with action makes a difference and setting **daily intentions** helps you be more in tune with your world and God's plan for you.

Not only will this bucket journal be a record of one year of hopes, dreams, struggles, and blessings, but it will also give you insight into how God works in your life through prayer.

My TALK with God today → **Day** **Date**

| ☐ Morning Prayer | ☐ Evening Prayer | **ASK IN FAITH** |

Three Things I am **THANKFUL** for Today:

1.

2.

3.

I turn this over to the Lord. **LET** go and let God handle it

What do I need forgiveness for?

Ask God to help with this challenge today.

Prayer with action makes a difference. I set these intentions for the day:

_____

_____

_____

_____

_____

Ask the Lord to bless these people today.

KEEP communicating with God today

Promptings from the Spirit   **Blessings I received today**

_____   _____

_____   _____

_____   _____

_____   _____

_____   _____

As I walk daily here on earth, Give me thy Spirit as I seek A change of heart, another birth, And grow, dear Lord, to be like thee.

Hymn 171

My TALK with God today → **Day**   **Date**

☐ Morning Prayer	☐ Evening Prayer

ASK IN FAITH

Three Things I am **THANKFUL** for Today:
1.
2.
3.

I turn this over to the Lord. **LET** go and let God handle it

What do I need forgiveness for?

Ask God to help with this challenge today.

Prayer with action makes a difference. I set these intentions for the day:

_____
_____
_____
_____
_____

Ask the Lord to bless these people today.

KEEP communicating with God today

Promptings from the Spirit	Blessings I received today
_____	_____
_____	_____
_____	_____
_____	_____
_____	_____

Behold, I have fasted and prayed many days that I might know these things of myself. And now I do know of myself that they are true; for the Lord God hath made them manifest unto me by his Holy Spirit; and this is the spirit of revelation which is in me.
Alma 5:46

My TALK with God today **Day**　　　　　**Date**

☐ Morning Prayer	☐ Evening Prayer

ASK IN FAITH

Three Things I am **THANKFUL** for Today:

1.

2.

3.

What do I need forgiveness for?

I turn this over to the Lord. **LET** go and let God handle it

Ask God to help with this challenge today.

Prayer with action makes a difference. I set these intentions for the day:

_____

_____

_____

_____

_____

Ask the Lord to bless these people today.

KEEP communicating with God today

Promptings from the Spirit　　　**Blessings I received today**

_____　_____

_____　_____

_____　_____

_____　_____

_____　_____

But this is not all; they had given themselves to much prayer, and fasting.
Alma 17:3

My TALK with God today ➡ **Day**   **Date**

☐ Morning Prayer	☐ Evening Prayer

ASK IN FAITH

Three Things I am **THANKFUL** for Today:
1.
2.
3.

I turn this over to the Lord. **LET** go and let God handle it

What do I need forgiveness for?

Ask God to help with this challenge today.

Prayer with action makes a difference. I set these intentions for the day:

_____

_____

_____

_____

_____

Ask the Lord to bless these people today.

KEEP communicating with God today

Promptings from the Spirit	Blessings I received today
_____	_____
_____	_____
_____	_____
_____	_____
_____	_____

Ere you left your room this morning, Did you think to pray? In the name of Christ, our Savior, Did you sue for loving favor As a shield today?
Hymn 140

My TALK with God today ➤ **Day** **Date**

☐ Morning Prayer ☐ Evening Prayer

ASK IN FAITH

Three Things I am **THANKFUL** for Today:
1.
2.
3.

I turn this over to the Lord. **LET** go and let God handle it

What do I need forgiveness for?

Ask God to help with this challenge today.

Prayer with action makes a difference. I set these intentions for the day:

_____

_____

_____

_____

_____

Ask the Lord to bless these people today.

KEEP communicating with God today

Promptings from the Spirit | Blessings I received today

_____ | _____

_____ | _____

_____ | _____

_____ | _____

_____ | _____

I stand all amazed at the love Jesus offers me, Confused at the grace that so fully he proffers me. I tremble to know that for me he was crucified, that for me, a sinner, he suffered, he bled and died.
Hymn 193

My TALK with God today **Day**   **Date**

☐ Morning Prayer	☐ Evening Prayer

Three Things I am **THANKFUL** for Today:
1.
2.
3.

I turn this over to the Lord. **LET** go and let God handle it

What do I need forgiveness for?

Ask God to help with this challenge today.

Prayer with action makes a difference. I set these intentions for the day:

_____

_____

_____

_____

_____

Ask the Lord to bless these people today.

KEEP communicating with God today

Promptings from the Spirit	Blessings I received today
_____	_____
_____	_____
_____	_____
_____	_____
_____	_____

I would exhort you that ye would ask God, the Eternal Father, in the name of Christ, if these things are not true; and if ye shall ask with a sincere heart, with real intent, having faith in Christ, he will manifest the truth of it unto you, by the power of the Holy Ghost. Moroni 10:4

My TALK with God today   **Day**   **Date**

☐ Morning Prayer	☐ Evening Prayer

ASK IN FAITH

Three Things I am **THANKFUL** for Today:

1.

2.

3.

What do I need forgiveness for?

Turn this over to the Lord. **LET** go and let God handle it

Ask God to help with this challenge today.

Prayer with action makes a difference. I set these intentions for the day:

_____

_____

_____

_____

_____

Ask the Lord to bless these people today.

KEEP communicating with God today

Promptings from the Spirit   **Blessings I received today**

_____   _____

_____   _____

_____   _____

_____   _____

_____   _____

I, the Lord, will forgive whom I will forgive, but of you it is required to forgive all men.
D&C 64:10

My TALK with God today → **Day**   **Date**

❑ Morning Prayer	❑ Evening Prayer

Three Things I am **THANKFUL** for Today:
1.
2.
3.

Turn this over to the Lord. **LET** go and let God handle it

Prayer with action makes a difference. I set these intentions for the day:

_____

_____

_____

_____

_____

KEEP communicating with God today

Promptings from the Spirit   Blessings I received today

_____ _____

_____ _____

_____ _____

_____ _____

_____ _____

ASK IN FAITH

What do I need forgiveness for?

Ask God to help with this challenge today.

Ask the Lord to bless these people today.

Let every man be swift to hear, slow to speak, slow to wrath.
James 1:19

My TALK with God today → **Day** **Date**

☐ Morning Prayer	☐ Evening Prayer

ASK IN FAITH

Three Things I am **THANKFUL** for Today:

1.

2.

3.

What do I need
forgiveness for?

Turn this over to the Lord. **LET** go and let God handle it

Ask God to help with this
challenge today.

Prayer with action makes a difference. I set these intentions for the day:

_____

_____

_____

_____

_____

Ask the Lord to bless
these people today.

KEEP communicating with God today

Promptings from the Spirit	Blessings I received today
_____	_____
_____	_____
_____	_____
_____	_____
_____	_____

Pray unto the Father
with all the energy of
heart, that ye may be
filled with this love.
Moroni 7:48

My TALK with God today | **Day** | **Date**

☐ Morning Prayer	☐ Evening Prayer

ASK IN FAITH

Three Things I am **THANKFUL** for Today:

1.

2.

3.

Turn this over to the Lord. **LET** go and let God handle it

What do I need forgiveness for?

Ask God to help with this challenge today.

Prayer with action makes a difference. I set these intentions for the day:

_____

_____

_____

_____

_____

Ask the Lord to bless these people today.

KEEP communicating with God today

Promptings from the Spirit	Blessings I received today
_____	_____
_____	_____
_____	_____
_____	_____
_____	_____

Waiting upon the Lord implies continued obedience and spiritual progress toward Him. Waiting upon the Lord does not imply biding one's time. You should never feel like you are in a waiting room.
M. Russell Ballard

My TALK with God today | Day | Date

☐ Morning Prayer	☐ Evening Prayer

ASK IN FAITH

Three Things I am **THANKFUL** for Today:

1.

2.

3.

What do I need forgiveness for?

Turn this over to the Lord. **LET** go and let God handle it

Ask God to help with this challenge today.

Prayer with action makes a difference. I set these intentions for the day:

_____

_____

_____

_____

_____

Ask the Lord to bless these people today.

KEEP communicating with God today

Promptings from the Spirit	Blessings I received today
_____	_____
_____	_____
_____	_____
_____	_____
_____	_____

Yea, and when you do not cry unto the Lord, let your hearts be full, drawn out in prayer unto him continually for your welfare, and also for the welfare of those who are around you.

Alma 34:27

My TALK with God today **Day** | **Date**

☐ Morning Prayer ☐ Evening Prayer | **ASK IN FAITH**

Three Things I am **THANKFUL** for Today:

1.

2.

3.

Turn this over to the Lord. **LET** go and let God handle it

What do I need forgiveness for?

Ask God to help with this challenge today.

Prayer with action makes a difference. I set these intentions for the day:

_____

_____

_____

_____

_____

Ask the Lord to bless these people today.

KEEP communicating with God today

Promptings from the Spirit | Blessings I received today

_____ _____

_____ _____

_____ _____

_____ _____

_____ _____

"A man with God is always in the majority."
John Knox

My TALK with God today   **Day**   **Date**

☐ Morning Prayer	☐ Evening Prayer	**ASK IN FAITH**

Three Things I am **THANKFUL** for Today:	**What do I need forgiveness for?**
1.	
2.	
3.	

Turn this over to the Lord. **LET** go and let God handle it

Ask God to help with this challenge today.

Prayer with action makes a difference. I set these intentions for the day:

_____

_____   Ask the Lord to bless these people today.

_____

_____

_____

KEEP communicating with God today

Promptings from the Spirit   Blessings I received today

_____   _____

_____   _____   "All I am, or can be, I owe to my angel mother."
Abraham Lincoln

_____   _____

_____   _____

_____   _____

My TALK with God today **Day**   **Date**

☐ Morning Prayer	☐ Evening Prayer	**ASK IN FAITH**

Three Things I am **THANKFUL** for Today:

1.

2.

3.

Turn this over to the Lord. **LET** go and let God handle it

ASK IN FAITH

What do I need forgiveness for?

Ask God to help with this challenge today.

Prayer with action makes a difference. I set these intentions for the day:

_____

_____

_____

_____

_____

Ask the Lord to bless these people today.

KEEP communicating with God today

Promptings from the Spirit	Blessings I received today
_____	_____
_____	_____
_____	_____
_____	_____
_____	_____

Strait is the gate, and narrow is the way, which leadeth unto life, and few there be that find it.
Matthew 7:13-14

My TALK with God today → **Day** **Date**

❑ **Morning Prayer**   ❑ **Evening Prayer**

ASK IN FAITH

Three Things I am **THANKFUL** for Today:

1.

2.

3.

Turn this over to the Lord. **LET** go and let God handle it

What do I need forgiveness for?

Ask God to help with this challenge today.

Prayer with action makes a difference. I set these intentions for the day:

_____

_____

_____

_____

_____

Ask the Lord to bless these people today.

KEEP communicating with God today

Promptings from the Spirit   Blessings I received today

_____   _____

_____   _____

_____   _____

_____   _____

_____   _____

"Because we have the truth about the Godhead and our relationship to Them, the purpose of life, and the nature of our eternal destiny, we have the ultimate road map and assurance for our journey through mortality."
Dallin H Oaks

My TALK with God today ➤ **Day**   **Date**

☐ Morning Prayer	☐ Evening Prayer	**ASK IN FAITH**

Three Things I am **THANKFUL** for Today:

1.

2.

3.

I turn this over to the Lord. **LET** go and let God handle it

What do I need forgiveness for?

Ask God to help with this challenge today.

Prayer with action makes a difference. I set these intentions for the day:

_____

_____

_____

_____

_____

Ask the Lord to bless these people today..

KEEP communicating with God today

Promptings from the Spirit   Blessings I received today

_____   _____

_____   _____

_____   _____

_____   _____

_____   _____

Come boldly [to] the throne of grace, and fall at the feet of the Holy One of Israel. Come and feast "without money and without price" at the table of the Lord. Jeffrey R. Holland

My TALK with God today　　**Day**　　　　　　　**Date**

☐ Morning Prayer	☐ Evening Prayer

ASK IN FAITH

Three Things I am **THANKFUL** for Today:

1.

2.

3.

What do I need forgiveness for?

I turn this over to the Lord. **LET** go and let God handle it

Ask God to help with this challenge today.

Prayer with action makes a difference. I set these intentions for the day:

_____

_____

_____

_____

_____

Ask the Lord to bless these people today..

KEEP communicating with God today

Promptings from the Spirit　　**Blessings I received today**

_____　　_____

_____　　_____

_____　　_____

_____　　_____

_____　　_____

"Family is not an important thing. It's everything."
Michael J. Fox

My TALK with God today → **Day**   **Date**

☐ **Morning Prayer**   ☐ **Evening Prayer**

Three Things I am **THANKFUL** for Today:

1.

2.

3.

I turn this over to the Lord. **LET** go and let God handle it

Prayer with action makes a difference. I set these intentions for the day:

_____

_____

_____

_____

_____

KEEP communicating with God today

Promptings from the Spirit   **Blessings I received today**

_____   _____

_____   _____

_____   _____

_____   _____

_____   _____

ASK IN FAITH

What do I need forgiveness for?

Ask God to help with this challenge today.

Ask the Lord to bless these people today..

"Family life is the best method for achieving happiness in this world, and it is a clear pattern given to us from the Lord about what is to be in the next world."
Spencer W. Kimball

My TALK with God today → Day   Date

☐ Morning Prayer	☐ Evening Prayer	**ASK IN FAITH**

Three Things I am **THANKFUL** for Today:

What do I need forgiveness for?

1.

2.

3.

I turn this over to the Lord. **LET** go and let God handle it

Ask God to help with this challenge today.

Prayer with action makes a difference. I set these intentions for the day:

_____

_____   **Ask the Lord to bless these people today..**

_____

_____

_____

KEEP communicating with God today

Promptings from the Spirit	Blessings I received today
_____	_____
_____	_____
_____	_____
_____	_____
_____	_____

"First promptings are pure inspiration from heaven. When they confirm or testify to us, we need to recognize them for what they are and never let them slip past"
Ronald A Rasband

My TALK with God today	Day	Date

☐ **Morning Prayer**	☐ **Evening Prayer**	**ASK IN FAITH**

Three Things I am **THANKFUL** for Today:	**What do I need forgiveness for?**
1.	
2.	
3.	

I turn this over to the Lord. **LET** go and let God handle it	**Ask God to help with this challenge today.**

Prayer with action makes a difference. I set these intentions for the day:

_____

_____   **Ask the Lord to bless these people today..**

_____

_____

_____

KEEP communicating with God today

Promptings from the Spirit   **Blessings I received today**

_____   _____

_____   _____

_____   _____

_____   _____

_____   _____

"For our own good, we need the moral courage to forgive and to ask for forgiveness. Never is the soul nobler and more courageous than when we forgive. This includes forgiving ourselves."
Dieter F Uchtdorf

My TALK with God today → **Day** **Date**

☐ Morning Prayer	☐ Evening Prayer

ASK IN FAITH

What do I need forgiveness for?

Three Things I am **THANKFUL** for Today:

1.

2.

3.

I turn this over to the Lord. **LET** go and let God handle it

Ask God to help with this challenge today.

Prayer with action makes a difference. I set these intentions for the day:

_____

_____

_____

_____

_____

Ask the Lord to bless these people today..

KEEP communicating with God today

Promptings from the Spirit	Blessings I received today
_____	_____
_____	_____
_____	_____
_____	_____
_____	_____

"God's plan provides a way for family relationships to extend beyond the grave. We can return to the presence of God, eternally united with our families."
Quentin L. Cook

My TALK with God today | **Day** | **Date**

☐ Morning Prayer	☐ Evening Prayer

ASK IN FAITH

Three Things I am **THANKFUL** for Today:

1.

2.

3.

I turn this over to the Lord. **LET** go and let God handle it

What do I need forgiveness for?

Ask God to help with this challenge today.

Prayer with action makes a difference. I set these intentions for the day:

_____

_____

_____

_____

_____

Ask the Lord to bless these people today..

KEEP communicating with God today

Promptings from the Spirit	Blessings I received today
_____	_____
_____	_____
_____	_____
_____	_____
_____	_____

"How do we know the things of the Spirit? How do we know that it is from God? By the fruits of it."
Gordon B Hinckley

My TALK with God today ➤ **Day**   **Date**

☐ **Morning Prayer**   ☐ **Evening Prayer**

ASK IN FAITH

Three Things I am **THANKFUL** for Today:

1.

2.

3.

What do I need forgiveness for?

I turn this over to the Lord. **LET** go and let God handle it

Ask God to help with this challenge today.

Prayer with action makes a difference. I set these intentions for the day:

_____

_____

_____

_____

_____

Ask the Lord to bless these people today..

KEEP communicating with God today

Promptings from the Spirit   **Blessings I received today**

_____ _____

_____ _____

_____ _____

_____ _____

_____ _____

"In a world of turmoil and uncertainty, it is more important than ever to make our families the center of our lives and the top of our priorities."
L. Tom Perry

My TALK with God today ➤ **Day** **Date**

☐ Morning Prayer	☐ Evening Prayer

ASK IN FAITH

Three Things I am **THANKFUL** for Today:

1.

2.

3.

I turn this over to the Lord. **LET** go and let God handle it

What do I need forgiveness for?

Ask God to help with this challenge today.

Prayer with action makes a difference. I set these intentions for the day:

_____

_____

_____

_____

_____

Ask the Lord to bless these people today..

KEEP communicating with God today

Promptings from the Spirit	Blessings I received today
_____	_____
_____	_____
_____	_____
_____	_____
_____	_____

"In the Lord's own way and time, no blessing will be withheld from His faithful Saints. The Lord will judge and reward each individual according to heartfelt desire as well as deed."
Russell M Nelson

My TALK with God today	Day	Date

☐ Morning Prayer	☐ Evening Prayer	ASK IN FAITH

Three Things I am THANKFUL for Today:

What do I need forgiveness for?

1.

2.

3.

I turn this over to the Lord. **LET** go and let God handle it

Ask God to help with this challenge today.

Prayer with action makes a difference. I set these intentions for the day:

_____

_____

_____

_____

_____

Ask the Lord to bless these people today.

KEEP communicating with God today

Promptings from the Spirit	Blessings I received today
_____	_____
_____	_____
_____	_____
_____	_____
_____	_____

"Let us be more determined to make [righteous] homes, to be kinder husbands, more thoughtful wives, more exemplary to our children, determined that in our homes we are going to have just a little taste of heaven here on this earth."
David O. McKay

My TALK with God today **Day** **Date**

❑ **Morning Prayer** | ❑ **Evening Prayer**

ASK IN FAITH

Three Things I am **THANKFUL** for Today:

1.

2.

3.

I turn this over to the Lord. **LET** go and let God handle it

What do I need forgiveness for?

Ask God to help with this challenge today.

Prayer with action makes a difference. I set these intentions for the day:

_____

_____

_____

_____

_____

Ask the Lord to bless these people today.

KEEP communicating with God today

Promptings from the Spirit **Blessings I received today**

_____ _____

_____ _____

_____ _____

_____ _____

_____

"Our covenant commitment to Him permits our Heavenly Father to let His divine influence, 'the power of godliness' flow into our lives.
D Todd Christopherson

My TALK with God today   **Day**   **Date**

☐ Morning Prayer	☐ Evening Prayer	**ASK IN FAITH**

Three Things I am **THANKFUL** for Today:

What do I need forgiveness for?

1.

2.

3.

I turn this over to the Lord. **LET** go and let God handle it

Ask God to help with this challenge today.

Prayer with action makes a difference. I set these intentions for the day:

_____

_____

_____

_____

_____

Ask the Lord to bless these people today.

KEEP communicating with God today

Promptings from the Spirit   **Blessings I received today**

_____ _____

_____ _____

_____ _____

_____ _____

_____ _____

"Sometimes it is harder for us to smile at those who live with us, the immediate members of our families, than it is to smile at those who are not so close to us. Let us never forget: love begins at home."
Mother Teresa

My TALK with God today　　　**Day**　　　　　　　　**Date**

☐ Morning Prayer	☐ Evening Prayer	**ASK IN FAITH**

Three Things I am **THANKFUL** for Today:	**What do I need forgiveness for?**
1.	
2.	
3.	

I turn this over to the Lord. **LET** go and let God handle it

Ask God to help with this challenge today.

Prayer with action makes a difference. I set these intentions for the day:

_____

_____

_____

_____

_____

Ask the Lord to bless these people today.

KEEP communicating with God today

Promptings from the Spirit	Blessings I received today
_____	_____
_____	_____
_____	_____
_____	_____
_____	_____

"The family is one of God's greatest fortresses against the evils of our day. Help keep your family strong and close and worthy of our Father in Heaven's blessings. As you do, you will receive faith and strength which will bless your lives forever."
Ezra Taft Benson

My TALK with God today   **Day**   **Date**

❑ Morning Prayer	❑ Evening Prayer	**ASK IN FAITH**

Three Things I am THANKFUL for Today:

1.

2.

3.

I turn this over to the Lord. **LET** go and let God handle it

Prayer with action makes a difference. I set these intentions for the day:

_____

_____

_____

_____

_____

What do I need forgiveness for?

Ask God to help with this challenge today.

Ask the Lord to bless these people today.

KEEP communicating with God today

Promptings from the Spirit	Blessings I received today
_____	_____
_____	_____
_____	_____
_____	_____
_____	_____

"The first and best victory is to conquer self; to be conquered by self is, of all things, the most shameful and vile."
Plato

My TALK with God today   **Day**   **Date**

☐ Morning Prayer	☐ Evening Prayer

ASK IN FAITH

Three Things I am **THANKFUL** for Today:

1.

2.

3.

I turn this over to the Lord. **LET** go and let God handle it

What do I need forgiveness for?

Ask God to help with this challenge today.

Prayer with action makes a difference. I set these intentions for the day:

_____

_____

_____

_____

_____

Ask the Lord to bless these people today.

KEEP communicating with God today

Promptings from the Spirit	**Blessings I received today**
_____	_____
_____	_____
_____	_____
_____	_____

"The height of a man's success is gauged by his self-mastery; the depth of his failure by his self-abandonment. ... And this law is the expression of eternal justice. He who cannot establish dominion over himself will have no dominion over others."
Da Vinci

My TALK with God today   Day   Date

☐ Morning Prayer	☐ Evening Prayer

ASK IN FAITH

Three Things I am THANKFUL for Today:

1.

2.

3.

What do I need forgiveness for?

I turn this over to the Lord. **LET** go and let God handle it

Ask God to help with this challenge today.

Prayer with action makes a difference. I set these intentions for the day:

_____

_____

_____

_____

_____

Ask the Lord to bless these people today.

KEEP communicating with God today

Promptings from the Spirit	Blessings I received today
_____	_____
_____	_____
_____	_____
_____	_____
_____	_____

"The key to strengthening our families is having the Spirit of the Lord come into our homes. The goal of our families is to be on the strait and narrow path."
Robert D. Hales

My TALK with God today

Day   **Date**

☐ **Morning Prayer**   ☐ **Evening Prayer**

Three Things I am **THANKFUL** for Today:
1.
2.
3.

I turn this over to the Lord. **LET** go and let God handle it

Prayer with action makes a difference. I set these intentions for the day:

_____

_____

_____

_____

_____

ASK IN FAITH

What do I need forgiveness for?

Ask God to help with this challenge today.

Ask the Lord to bless these people today.

KEEP communicating with God today

Promptings from the Spirit   **Blessings I received today**

_____   _____

_____   _____

_____   _____

_____   _____

_____   _____

"The Lord is good: Blessed is the man that trusteth in him."
Psalms 38:4

My TALK with God today

Day _____   **Date** _____

☐ Morning Prayer	☐ Evening Prayer

ASK IN FAITH

What do I need forgiveness for?

Three Things I am THANKFUL for Today:

1.
2.
3.

I turn this over to the Lord. **LET** go and let God handle it

Ask God to help with this challenge today.

Prayer with action makes a difference. I set these intentions for the day:

_____

_____

_____

_____

_____

Ask the Lord to bless these people today.

KEEP communicating with God today

Promptings from the Spirit   **Blessings I received today**

_____   _____

_____   _____

_____   _____

_____   _____

_____   _____

"We will receive the joy of forgiveness in our own lives when we are willing to extend that joy freely to others. Lip service is not enough. We need to purge our hearts and minds of feelings and thoughts of bitterness and let the light and the love of Christ enter in.
Dieter F Uchtdorf

My TALK with God today → **Day** **Date**

❑ Morning Prayer	❑ Evening Prayer	**ASK IN FAITH**

Three Things I am **THANKFUL** for Today:

1.

2.

3.

I turn this over to the Lord. **LET** go and let God handle it

What do I need forgiveness for?

Ask God to help with this challenge today.

Prayer with action makes a difference. I set these intentions for the day:

_____

_____

_____

_____

_____

Ask the Lord to bless these people today.

KEEP communicating with God today

Promptings from the Spirit	Blessings I received today
_____	_____
_____	_____
_____	_____
_____	_____
_____	_____

"What matters most is what lasts the longest, and our families are for eternity."
M. Russell Ballard

My TALK with God today　　　　　**Day**　　　　　　　　**Date**

☐ Morning Prayer	☐ Evening Prayer

ASK IN FAITH

Three Things I am **THANKFUL** for Today:
1.
2.
3.

I turn this over to the Lord. **LET** go and let God handle it

What do I need forgiveness for?

Ask God to help with this challenge today.

Prayer with action makes a difference. I set these intentions for the day:

_____

_____

_____

_____

_____

Ask the Lord to bless these people today.

KEEP communicating with God today

Promptings from the Spirit	Blessings I received today
_____	_____
_____	_____
_____	_____
_____	_____
_____	_____

"When we realize that parents and family members can be more than blood relations and are in very deed friends, then we will have a glimpse of how our Heavenly Father wants us to live, not only as brothers and sisters but as very close friends."
Marvin J. Ashton

My TALK with God today → **Day**   **Date**

☐ Morning Prayer	☐ Evening Prayer

ASK IN FAITH

Three Things I am **THANKFUL** for Today:
1.
2.
3.

What do I need forgiveness for?

I turn this over to the Lord. **LET** go and let God handle it

Ask God to help with this challenge today.

Prayer with action makes a difference. I set these intentions for the day:

_____

_____

_____

_____

_____

Ask the Lord to bless these people today.

KEEP communicating with God today

Promptings from the Spirit	Blessings I received today
_____	_____
_____	_____
_____	_____
_____	_____

"Yet I will rejoice in the Lord, I will joy in the God of my salvation." The Lord God is my strength, and he will make my feet … to walk upon mine high places." Habakkuk 3:18-19

My TALK with God today ➜ **Day** **Date**

☐ Morning Prayer ☐ Evening Prayer

ASK IN FAITH

Three Things I am **THANKFUL** for Today:

1.

2.

3.

I turn this over to the Lord. **LET** go and let God handle it

What do I need
forgiveness for?

Ask God to help with this
challenge today.

Prayer with action makes a difference. I set these
intentions for the day:

_____

_____

_____

_____

_____

Ask the Lord to bless
these people today.

KEEP communicating with God today

Promptings from the Spirit   Blessings I received today

_____   _____

_____   _____

_____   _____

_____   _____

_____   _____

And charity suffereth long,
and is kind, and envieth not,
and is not puffed up,
seeketh not her own, is not
easily provoked, thinketh
no evil, and rejoiceth not in
iniquity but rejoiceth in the
truth, beareth all things,
believeth all things, hopeth
all things, endureth all
things.
Moroni 7:45

My TALK with God today **Day** **Date**

☐ Morning Prayer ☐ Evening Prayer

ASK IN FAITH

Three Things I am **THANKFUL** for Today:

1.

2.

3.

I turn this over to the Lord. **LET** go and let God handle it

What do I need forgiveness for?

Ask God to help with this challenge today.

Prayer with action makes a difference. I set these intentions for the day:

_____

_____

_____

_____

_____

Ask the Lord to bless these people today.

KEEP communicating with God today

Promptings from the Spirit **Blessings I received today**

_____ _____

_____ _____

_____ _____

_____ _____

_____ _____

According to your faith be it unto you. Matthew 9:29

My TALK with God today → **Day**   **Date**

☐ Morning Prayer	☐ Evening Prayer	**ASK IN FAITH**

Three Things I am **THANKFUL** for Today:

1.

2.

3.

I turn this over to the Lord. **LET** go and let God handle it

What do I need forgiveness for?

Ask God to help with this challenge today.

Prayer with action makes a difference. I set these intentions for the day:

_____

_____

_____

_____

_____

Ask the Lord to bless these people today.

KEEP communicating with God today

Promptings from the Spirit   Blessings I received today

_____   _____

_____   _____

_____   _____

_____   _____

_____   _____

All men have their FEARS. But those who face their fears with FAITH have COURAGE as well.
Thomas S Monson

My TALK with God today → **Day**   **Date**

☐ Morning Prayer	☐ Evening Prayer

ASK IN FAITH

Three Things I am **THANKFUL** for Today:

1.

2.

3.

I turn this over to the Lord. **LET** go and let God handle it

What do I need forgiveness for?

Ask God to help with this challenge today.

Prayer with action makes a difference. I set these intentions for the day:

_____

_____

_____

_____

_____

Ask the Lord to bless these people today.

KEEP communicating with God today

Promptings from the Spirit   Blessings I received today

_____ _____

_____ _____

_____ _____

_____ _____

_____ _____

All the believers were one in heart and mind. No one claimed that any of their possessions was their own, but they shared everything they had.
Acts 4:32

My TALK with God today　　　　Day　　　　　　　　Date

☐ Morning Prayer	☐ Evening Prayer

ASK IN FAITH

Three Things I am **THANKFUL** for Today:
1.
2.
3.

What do I need forgiveness for?

I turn this over to the Lord. **LET** go and let God handle it

Ask God to help with this challenge today.

Prayer with action makes a difference. I set these intentions for the day:

_____

_____

_____

_____

_____

Ask the Lord to bless these people today.

KEEP communicating with God today

Promptings from the Spirit	Blessings I received today
_____	_____
_____	_____
_____	_____
_____	_____
_____	_____

And as many as should look upon that serpent should live, even so as many as should look upon the Son of God with faith, having a contrite spirit, might live, even unto that life which is eternal.
Helaman 8:15

My TALK with God today → **Day** **Date**

| ☐ Morning Prayer | ☐ Evening Prayer |

ASK IN FAITH

Three Things I am **THANKFUL** for Today:

1.

2.

3.

I turn this over to the Lord. **LET** go and let God handle it

What do I need forgiveness for?

Ask God to help with this challenge today.

Prayer with action makes a difference. I set these intentions for the day:

_____

_____

_____

_____

_____

Ask the Lord to bless these people today.

KEEP communicating with God today

Promptings from the Spirit   **Blessings I received today**

_____   _____

_____   _____

_____   _____

_____   _____

_____   _____

And that he manifesteth himself unto all those who believe in him, by the power of the Holy Ghost; yea, unto every nation, kindred, tongue, and people, working mighty miracles, signs, and wonders, among the children of men according to their faith.
2 Nephi 2+6:13

My TALK with God today → **Day** **Date**

☐ Morning Prayer	☐ Evening Prayer	**ASK IN FAITH**

Three Things I am **THANKFUL** for Today:

1.

2.

3.

Turn this over to the Lord. **LET** go and let God handle it

What do I need forgiveness for?

Ask God to help with this challenge today.

Prayer with action makes a difference. I set these intentions for the day:

_____

_____

_____

_____

_____

Ask the Lord to bless these people today.

KEEP communicating with God today

Promptings from the Spirit   Blessings I received today

_____   _____

_____   _____

_____   _____

_____   _____

_____   _____

All things were made by him; and without him was not any thing made that was made.
John 1:3

| My TALK with God today | Day | Date |

| ☐ Morning Prayer | ☐ Evening Prayer |

ASK IN FAITH

Three Things I am THANKFUL for Today:

1.

2.

3.

Turn this over to the Lord. **LET** go and let God handle it

What do I need forgiveness for?

Ask God to help with this challenge today.

Prayer with action makes a difference. I set these intentions for the day:

_____

_____

_____

_____

_____

Ask the Lord to bless these people today.

KEEP communicating with God today

| Promptings from the Spirit | Blessings I received today |

_____   _____

_____   _____

_____   _____

_____   _____

_____   _____

All those who accept the Savior's gracious gift of repentance and live His commandments will receive eternal life, even though they do not attain to all its characteristics and perfections in mortality.
M Russell Ballard

My TALK with God today → **Day** **Date**

☐ **Morning Prayer** ☐ **Evening Prayer**

ASK IN FAITH

Three Things I am **THANKFUL** for Today:

1.

2.

3.

Turn this over to the Lord. **LET** go and let God handle it

What do I need forgiveness for?

Ask God to help with this challenge today.

Prayer with action makes a difference. I set these intentions for the day:

_____

_____

_____

_____

_____

Ask the Lord to bless these people today.

KEEP communicating with God today

Promptings from the Spirit **Blessings I received today**

_____ _____

_____ _____

_____ _____

_____ _____

_____ _____

Always remember the promise of good things to come, both now and hereafter, for those who are firm and steadfast in the faith of Christ.
D. Todd Christofferson

My TALK with God today   **Day**   **Date**

❑ Morning Prayer	❑ Evening Prayer	**ASK IN FAITH**

Three Things I am **THANKFUL** for Today:

1.

2.

3.

Turn this over to the Lord. **LET** go and let God handle it

Prayer with action makes a difference. I set these intentions for the day:

_____

_____

_____

_____

_____

What do I need forgiveness for?

Ask God to help with this challenge today.

Ask the Lord to bless these people today.

KEEP communicating with God today

Promptings from the Spirit   Blessings I received today

_____   _____

_____   _____

_____   _____

_____   _____

_____   _____

And there were many whose faith was so exceedingly strong, even before Christ came, who could not be kept from within the veil, but truly saw with their eyes the things which they had beheld with an eye of faith, and they were glad. Ether 12:19

My TALK with God today   **Day**   **Date**

☐ Morning Prayer	☐ Evening Prayer

ASK IN FAITH

Three Things I am **THANKFUL** for Today:

1.

2.

3.

What do I need forgiveness for?

Turn this over to the Lord. **LET** go and let God handle it

Ask God to help with this challenge today.

Prayer with action makes a difference. I set these intentions for the day:

_____

_____

_____

_____

_____

Ask the Lord to bless these people today.

KEEP communicating with God today

Promptings from the Spirit	Blessings I received today
_____	_____
_____	_____
_____	_____
_____	_____
_____	_____

Am I the woman I think I am, the woman I want to be? More importantly, am I the woman the Savior needs me to be?
Sheri Dew

My TALK with God today **Day** **Date**

☐ **Morning Prayer** ☐ **Evening Prayer**

ASK IN FAITH

Three Things I am **THANKFUL** for Today:

1.

2.

3.

Turn this over to the Lord. **LET** go and let God handle it

What do I need forgiveness for?

Ask God to help with this challenge today.

Prayer with action makes a difference. I set these intentions for the day:

_____

_____

_____

_____

_____

Ask the Lord to bless these people today.

KEEP communicating with God today

Promptings from the Spirit   **Blessings I received today**

_____   _____

_____   _____

_____   _____

_____   _____

_____

An he leaping up stood, and walked, and entered with them into the temple, walking, and leaping, and praising God.
Acts 3:8

My TALK with God today **Day** **Date**

❏ **Morning Prayer** ❏ **Evening Prayer**

ASK IN FAITH

Three Things I am **THANKFUL** for Today:

What do I need forgiveness for?

1.

2.

3.

Turn this over to the Lord. **LET** go and let God handle it

Ask God to help with this challenge today.

Prayer with action makes a difference. I set these intentions for the day:

_____

_____

_____

_____

_____

Ask the Lord to bless these people today.

KEEP communicating with God today

Promptings from the Spirit   **Blessings I received today**

_____   _____

_____   _____

_____   _____

_____   _____

_____   _____

And as all have not faith, seek ye diligently and teach one another words of wisdom; yea, seek ye out of the best books words of wisdom; seek learning, even by study and also by faith. D&C 88:118

My TALK with God today ➤ **Day** **Date**

│ ☐ **Morning Prayer** │ ☐ **Evening Prayer** │

ASK IN FAITH

What do I need forgiveness for?

Three Things I am **THANKFUL** for Today:

1.

2.

3.

Turn this over to the Lord. **LET** go and let God handle it

Ask God to help with this challenge today.

Prayer with action makes a difference. I set these intentions for the day:

_____

_____

_____

_____

_____

Ask the Lord to bless these people today.

KEEP communicating with God today

Promptings from the Spirit	Blessings I received today
_____	_____
_____	_____
_____	_____
_____	_____
_____	_____

And as I partook of the fruit thereof it filled my soul with exceedingly great joy; wherefore, I began to be desirous that my family should partake of it also; for I knew that it was desirable above all other fruit.
1 Nephi 8:12

My TALK with God today   **Day**   **Date**

☐ Morning Prayer	☐ Evening Prayer	**ASK IN FAITH**

Three Things I am **THANKFUL** for Today:	**What do I need forgiveness for?**
1.	
2.	
3.	

Turn this over to the Lord. **LET** go and let God handle it

Ask God to help with this challenge today.

Prayer with action makes a difference. I set these intentions for the day:

_____

Ask the Lord to bless these people today.

_____

_____

_____

_____

KEEP communicating with God today

Promptings from the Spirit	Blessings I received today
_____	_____
_____	_____
_____	_____
_____	_____
_____	_____

Because we are the spirit children of God, everyone has a divine origin, nature, and potential. Each of us "is a beloved spirit son or daughter of heavenly parents." This is our identity! This is who we really are!
M Russell Ballard

My TALK with God today ➤ **Day** **Date**

| ☐ Morning Prayer | ☐ Evening Prayer | **ASK IN FAITH** |

Three Things I am **THANKFUL** for Today:

1.

2.

3.

I turn this over to the Lord. **LET** go and let God handle it

What do I need forgiveness for?

Ask God to help with this challenge today.

Prayer with action makes a difference. I set these intentions for the day:

_____

_____

_____

_____

_____

Ask the Lord to bless these people today..

KEEP communicating with God today

Promptings from the Spirit   Blessings I received today

_____   _____

_____   _____

_____   _____

_____   _____

_____   _____

And be ye kind one to another, tenderhearted, forgiving one another, even as God for Christ's sake hath forgiven you.
Ephesians 4:32

My TALK with God today   **Day**   **Date**

☐ Morning Prayer	☐ Evening Prayer	**ASK IN FAITH**

Three Things I am **THANKFUL** for Today:

1.

2.

3.

I turn this over to the Lord. **LET** go and let God handle it

Prayer with action makes a difference. I set these intentions for the day:

_____

_____

_____

_____

_____

What do I need forgiveness for?

Ask God to help with this challenge today.

Ask the Lord to bless these people today..

KEEP communicating with God today

Promptings from the Spirit	**Blessings I received today**
_____	_____
_____	_____
_____	_____
_____	_____
_____	_____

And Christ hath said: If ye will have faith in me ye shall have power to do whatsoever thing is expedient in me
Moroni 7:33

My TALK with God today

Day

Date

☐ Morning Prayer

☐ Evening Prayer

ASK IN FAITH

Three Things I am **THANKFUL** for Today:

1.

2.

3.

I turn this over to the Lord. **LET** go and let God handle it

What do I need forgiveness for?

Ask God to help with this challenge today.

Prayer with action makes a difference. I set these intentions for the day:

_____

_____

_____

_____

_____

Ask the Lord to bless these people today..

KEEP communicating with God today

Promptings from the Spirit

Blessings I received today

_____ _____

_____ _____

_____ _____

_____ _____

_____ _____

And God is able to make all grace abound toward you; that ye, always having all sufficiency in all things, may abound to every good work.
2 Corinthians 9:8

My TALK with God today → **Day**   **Date**

☐ Morning Prayer	☐ Evening Prayer

ASK IN FAITH

Three Things I am **THANKFUL** for Today:

1.

2.

3.

What do I need forgiveness for?

I turn this over to the Lord. **LET** go and let God handle it

Ask God to help with this challenge today.

Prayer with action makes a difference. I set these intentions for the day:

_____

_____

_____

_____

_____

Ask the Lord to bless these people today..

KEEP communicating with God today

Promptings from the Spirit	Blessings I received today
_____	_____
_____	_____
_____	_____
_____	_____
_____	_____

And I was led by the spirit, not knowing beforehand the things which I should do.
1 Nephi 4:6

My TALK with God today	Day		Date

☐ Morning Prayer	☐ Evening Prayer	**ASK IN FAITH**

Three Things I am **THANKFUL** for Today:	**What do I need forgiveness for?**
1.	
2.	
3.	

I turn this over to the Lord. **LET** go and let God handle it

Ask God to help with this challenge today.

Prayer with action makes a difference. I set these intentions for the day:

_____

_____

_____

Ask the Lord to bless these people today..

_____

_____

KEEP communicating with God today

Promptings from the Spirit   Blessings I received today

_____   _____

_____   _____

_____   _____

_____   _____

_____   _____

Do not be anxious about anything, but in every situation, by prayer and petition, with thanksgiving, present your requests to God. And the peace of God, which transcends all understanding, will guard your hearts and your minds in Christ Jesus.
Philippians 4:6-7

My TALK with God today | Day | Date

| ☐ Morning Prayer | ☐ Evening Prayer | **ASK IN FAITH** |

Three Things I am **THANKFUL** for Today:

What do I need forgiveness for?

1.

2.

3.

I turn this over to the Lord. **LET** go and let God handle it

Ask God to help with this challenge today.

Prayer with action makes a difference. I set these intentions for the day:

_____

_____

_____

_____

_____

Ask the Lord to bless these people today..

KEEP communicating with God today

Promptings from the Spirit | Blessings I received today

_____ _____

_____ _____

_____ _____

_____ _____

_____ _____

And it shall come to pass, that whosoever shall call on the name of the Lord shall be saved.
Acts 2:21

My TALK with God today	Day	Date

☐ Morning Prayer	☐ Evening Prayer	**ASK IN FAITH**

Three Things I am **THANKFUL** for Today:	**What do I need forgiveness for?**
1.	
2.	
3.	

I turn this over to the Lord. **LET** go and let God handle it

Ask God to help with this challenge today.

Prayer with action makes a difference. I set these intentions for the day:

_____

_____

_____

_____

_____

Ask the Lord to bless these people today..

KEEP communicating with God today

Promptings from the Spirit	Blessings I received today
_____	_____
_____	_____
_____	_____
_____	_____
_____	_____

And let us not be weary in well doing: for in due season we shall reap, if we faint not.
Galatians 6:9

My TALK with God today → **Day** **Date**

☐ Morning Prayer	☐ Evening Prayer

Three Things I am **THANKFUL** for Today:
1.
2.
3.

I turn this over to the Lord. **LET** go and let God handle it

Prayer with action makes a difference. I set these intentions for the day:

_____

_____

_____

_____

_____

KEEP communicating with God today

Promptings from the Spirit	Blessings I received today
_____	_____
_____	_____
_____	_____
_____	_____
_____	_____

ASK IN FAITH

What do I need forgiveness for?

Ask God to help with this challenge today.

Ask the Lord to bless these people today..

And neither at any time hath any wrought miracles until after their faith; wherefore they first believed in the Son of God
Ether 12:18

My TALK with God today | Day | Date

| ☐ Morning Prayer | ☐ Evening Prayer |

ASK IN FAITH

| Three Things I am **THANKFUL** for Today: |
| 1. |
| 2. |
| 3. |

What do I need forgiveness for?

I turn this over to the Lord. **LET** go and let God handle it

Ask God to help with this challenge today.

Prayer with action makes a difference. I set these intentions for the day:

_____

_____

_____

_____

_____

Ask the Lord to bless these people today..

KEEP communicating with God today

Promptings from the Spirit	Blessings I received today
_____	_____
_____	_____
_____	_____
_____	_____
_____	_____

And now behold, I say unto you, my brethren, if ye have experienced a change of heart, and if ye have felt to sing the song of redeeming love, I would ask, can ye feel so now?
Alma 5:26

My TALK with God today → Day   Date

☐ Morning Prayer	☐ Evening Prayer

ASK IN FAITH

Three Things I am **THANKFUL** for Today:

1.

2.

3.

What do I need forgiveness for?

I turn this over to the Lord. **LET** go and let God handle it

Ask God to help with this challenge today.

Prayer with action makes a difference. I set these intentions for the day:

_____

_____

_____

_____

_____

Ask the Lord to bless these people today.

KEEP communicating with God today

Promptings from the Spirit   **Blessings I received today**

_____   _____

_____   _____

_____   _____

_____   _____

_____   _____

And now abideth faith, hope, charity, these three; but the greatest of these is charity.
1 Corinthians 13:13

My TALK with God today   **Day**   **Date**

| ☐ Morning Prayer | ☐ Evening Prayer | **ASK IN FAITH** |

Three Things I am **THANKFUL** for Today:

What do I need forgiveness for?

1.

2.

3.

I turn this over to the Lord. **LET** go and let God handle it

Ask God to help with this challenge today.

Prayer with action makes a difference. I set these intentions for the day:

_____

_____

_____

_____

_____

Ask the Lord to bless these people today.

KEEP communicating with God today

Promptings from the Spirit   **Blessings I received today**

_____   _____

_____   _____

_____   _____

_____   _____

_____   _____

And now, as ye are desirous to come into the fold of God, and to be called his people, and are willing to bear one another's burdens, that they may be light.
Mosiah 18:8

My TALK with God today → Day   Date

☐ Morning Prayer	☐ Evening Prayer	**ASK IN FAITH**

Three Things I am **THANKFUL** for Today:

What do I need forgiveness for?

1.

2.

3.

I turn this over to the Lord. **LET** go and let God handle it

Ask God to help with this challenge today.

Prayer with action makes a difference. I set these intentions for the day:

_____

_____

Ask the Lord to bless these people today.

_____

_____

KEEP communicating with God today

Promptings from the Spirit	**Blessings I received today**
_____	_____
_____	_____
_____	_____
_____	_____

And now, because of the covenant which ye have made ye shall be called the children of Christ, his sons, and his daughters.
Mosiah 5:7

My TALK with God today   **Day**   **Date**

☐ Morning Prayer	☐ Evening Prayer

ASK IN FAITH

Three Things I am **THANKFUL** for Today:

1.

2.

3.

What do I need forgiveness for?

I turn this over to the Lord. **LET** go and let God handle it

Ask God to help with this challenge today.

Prayer with action makes a difference. I set these intentions for the day:

_____

_____

_____

_____

_____

Ask the Lord to bless these people today.

KEEP communicating with God today

Promptings from the Spirit   **Blessings I received today**

_____   _____

_____   _____

_____   _____

_____   _____

_____   _____

And oh, what joy, and what marvelous light I did behold; yea, my soul was filled with joy as exceeding as was my pain!
Alma 36:20

| My TALK with God today | Day | Date |

| Morning Prayer | Evening Prayer |

ASK IN FAITH

Three Things I am **THANKFUL** for Today:

What do I need forgiveness for?

1.

2.

3.

I turn this over to the Lord. **LET** go and let God handle it

Ask God to help with this challenge today.

Prayer with action makes a difference. I set these intentions for the day:

_____

_____

Ask the Lord to bless these people today.

_____

_____

_____

KEEP communicating with God today

Promptings from the Spirit

Blessings I received today

_____ _____

_____ _____

_____ _____

_____ _____

_____ _____

And see that ye have faith, hope, and charity, and then ye will always abound in good works.
Alma 7:24

My TALK with God today → **Day** **Date**

☐ Morning Prayer	☐ Evening Prayer

ASK IN FAITH

Three Things I am **THANKFUL** for Today:

1.

2.

3.

I turn this over to the Lord. **LET** go and let God handle it

What do I need forgiveness for?

Ask God to help with this challenge today.

Prayer with action makes a difference. I set these intentions for the day:

_____

_____

_____

_____

_____

Ask the Lord to bless these people today.

KEEP communicating with God today

Promptings from the Spirit   **Blessings I received today**

_____ _____

_____ _____

_____ _____

_____ _____

And the fruit of righteousness is sown in peace of them that make peace.
James 3:18

My TALK with God today ➤ Day ___ Date ___

☐ Morning Prayer	☐ Evening Prayer

ASK IN FAITH

Three Things I am **THANKFUL** for Today:

1.

2.

3.

What do I need forgiveness for?

I turn this over to the Lord. **LET** go and let God handle it

Ask God to help with this challenge today.

Prayer with action makes a difference. I set these intentions for the day:

_____

_____

_____

_____

_____

Ask the Lord to bless these people today.

KEEP communicating with God today

Promptings from the Spirit	Blessings I received today
_____	_____
_____	_____
_____	_____
_____	_____
_____	_____

And the Lord, he it is that doth go before thee; he will be with thee, he will not fail thee, neither forsake thee: fear not, neither be dismayed.
Deuteronomy 31:8

My TALK with God today ➤ **Day** | **Date**

| ☐ Morning Prayer | ☐ Evening Prayer |

ASK IN FAITH

Three Things I am **THANKFUL** for Today:

1.

2.

3.

What do I need forgiveness for?

I turn this over to the Lord. **LET** go and let God handle it

Ask God to help with this challenge today.

Prayer with action makes a difference. I set these intentions for the day:

_____

_____

_____

_____

_____

Ask the Lord to bless these people today.

KEEP communicating with God today

Promptings from the Spirit | **Blessings I received today**

_____ | _____

_____ | _____

_____ | _____

_____ | _____

_____ | _____

And then, if thou endure it well, God shall exalt thee on high; thou shalt triumph over all thy foes.
D&C 121:8

My TALK with God today → **Day** **Date**

☐ Morning Prayer	☐ Evening Prayer

Three Things I am **THANKFUL** for Today:

1.

2.

3.

I turn this over to the Lord. **LET** go and let God handle it

Prayer with action makes a difference. I set these intentions for the day:

_____

_____

_____

_____

_____

KEEP communicating with God today

Promptings from the Spirit   Blessings I received today

_____   _____

_____   _____

_____   _____

_____   _____

_____   _____

ASK IN FAITH

What do I need forgiveness for?

Ask God to help with this challenge today.

Ask the Lord to bless these people today.

And this is the confidence that we have in him, that, if we ask any thing according to his will, he heareth us.
1 John 5:14

My TALK with God today   **Day**   **Date**

☐ Morning Prayer	☐ Evening Prayer	ASK IN FAITH

Three Things I am **THANKFUL** for Today:

1.

2.

3.

I turn this over to the Lord. **LET** go and let God handle it

What do I need forgiveness for?

Ask God to help with this challenge today.

Prayer with action makes a difference. I set these intentions for the day:

_____

_____

_____

_____

_____

Ask the Lord to bless these people today.

KEEP communicating with God today

Promptings from the Spirit	Blessings I received today
_____	_____
_____	_____
_____	_____
_____	_____
_____	_____

And thou shalt love the Lord thy God with all thy heart, and with all thy soul, and with all thy mind, and with all thy strength, this is the first commandment.
Mark 12:30

My TALK with God today ➤ **Day**   **Date**

❑ Morning Prayer	❑ Evening Prayer

Three Things I am **THANKFUL** for Today:

1.

2.

3.

I turn this over to the Lord. **LET** go and let God handle it

What do I need forgiveness for?

Ask God to help with this challenge today.

Prayer with action makes a difference. I set these intentions for the day:

_____

_____

_____

_____

_____

Ask the Lord to bless these people today.

KEEP communicating with God today

Promptings from the Spirit	**Blessings I received today**
_____	_____
_____	_____
_____	_____
_____	_____
_____	_____

And we know that all things work together for good to them that love God, to them who are the called according to his purpose.
Romans 8:28

My TALK with God today **Day**　　　　　　**Date**

☐ Morning Prayer	☐ Evening Prayer	**ASK IN FAITH**

Three Things I am **THANKFUL** for Today:
1.
2.
3.

What do I need forgiveness for?

I turn this over to the Lord. **LET** go and let God handle it

Ask God to help with this challenge today.

Prayer with action makes a difference. I set these intentions for the day:

_____

_____

_____

_____

_____

Ask the Lord to bless these people today.

KEEP communicating with God today

Promptings from the Spirit　　**Blessings I received today**

_____　_____

_____　_____

_____　_____

_____　_____

_____　_____

And whatsoever ye do, do it heartily, as to the Lord, and not unto men; Knowing that of the Lord ye shall receive the reward of the inheritance: for ye serve the Lord Christ. Colossians 3:23-24

My TALK with God today **Day** **Date**

☐ **Morning Prayer**   ☐ **Evening Prayer**

ASK IN FAITH

Three Things I am **THANKFUL** for Today:

What do I need forgiveness for?

1.

2.

3.

I turn this over to the Lord. **LET** go and let God handle it

Ask God to help with this challenge today.

Prayer with action makes a difference. I set these intentions for the day:

_____

_____

Ask the Lord to bless these people today.

_____

_____

_____

KEEP communicating with God today

Promptings from the Spirit   Blessings I received today

_____ _____

_____ _____

_____ _____

_____ _____

_____ _____

And when ye stand praying, forgive, if ye have ought against any: that your Father also which is in heaven may forgive you your trespasses. Mark 11:25

My TALK with God today → **Day**   **Date**

☐   **Morning Prayer**   ☐   **Evening Prayer**

ASK IN FAITH

Three Things I am **THANKFUL** for Today:

1.

2.

3.

I turn this over to the Lord. **LET** go and let God handle it

What do I need forgiveness for?

Ask God to help with this challenge today.

Prayer with action makes a difference. I set these intentions for the day:

_____

_____

_____

_____

_____

Ask the Lord to bless these people today.

KEEP communicating with God today

Promptings from the Spirit   **Blessings I received today**

_____   _____

_____   _____

_____   _____

_____   _____

_____   _____

And ye ought to say in your hearts—let God judge between me and thee, and reward thee according to thy deeds.
D&C 64:11

My TALK with God today ➤ **Day**   **Date**

☐   **Morning Prayer**   ☐   **Evening Prayer**

ASK IN FAITH

Three Things I am **THANKFUL** for Today:

1.

2.

3.

I turn this over to the Lord. **LET** go and let God handle it

What do I need forgiveness for?

Ask God to help with this challenge today.

Prayer with action makes a difference. I set these intentions for the day:

_____

_____

_____

_____

_____

Ask the Lord to bless these people today.

KEEP communicating with God today

Promptings from the Spirit   **Blessings I received today**

_____   _____

_____   _____

_____   _____

_____   _____

_____   _____

And ye shall offer for a sacrifice unto me a broken heart and a contrite spirit.
3 Nephi 9:20

My TALK with God today   **Day**   **Date**

| ☐ Morning Prayer | ☐ Evening Prayer | **ASK IN FAITH** |

Three Things I am **THANKFUL** for Today:
1.
2.
3.

What do I need forgiveness for?

I turn this over to the Lord. **LET** go and let God handle it

Ask God to help with this challenge today.

Prayer with action makes a difference. I set these intentions for the day:

_____

_____

_____

_____

_____

Ask the Lord to bless these people today.

KEEP communicating with God today

Promptings from the Spirit   **Blessings I received today**

_____   _____

_____   _____

_____   _____

_____   _____

_____   _____

And ye shall seek me, and find me, when ye shall search for me with all your heart.
Jeremiah 29:13

My TALK with God today → **Day**   **Date**

❑ Morning Prayer	❑ Evening Prayer

ASK IN FAITH

Three Things I am **THANKFUL** for Today:

1.

2.

3.

I turn this over to the Lord. **LET** go and let God handle it

What do I need forgiveness for?

Ask God to help with this challenge today.

Prayer with action makes a difference. I set these intentions for the day:

_____

_____

_____

_____

_____

Ask the Lord to bless these people today.

KEEP communicating with God today

Promptings from the Spirit	Blessings I received today
_____	_____
_____	_____
_____	_____
_____	_____
_____	_____

Ask, and it shall be given you; seek, and ye shall find; knock, and it shall be opened unto you.
Matthew 7:7

My TALK with God today → **Day**   **Date**

☐ Morning Prayer	☐ Evening Prayer

ASK IN FAITH

Three Things I am **THANKFUL** for Today:
1.
2.
3.

I turn this over to the Lord. **LET** go and let God handle it

What do I need forgiveness for?

Ask God to help with this challenge today.

Prayer with action makes a difference. I set these intentions for the day:

_____

_____

_____

_____

_____

Ask the Lord to bless these people today.

KEEP communicating with God today

Promptings from the Spirit	Blessings I received today
_____	_____
_____	_____
_____	_____
_____	_____
_____	_____

At night, when I'm alone in bed, I close my eyes and see The many things I'm thankful for That God has given me.
CSB Pg 11

My TALK with God today → **Day** **Date**

☐ **Morning Prayer**	☐ **Evening Prayer**

ASK IN FAITH

Three Things I am **THANKFUL** for Today:

1.

2.

3.

What do I need forgiveness for?

Turn this over to the Lord. **LET** go and let God handle it

Ask God to help with this challenge today.

Prayer with action makes a difference. I set these intentions for the day:

_____

_____

_____

_____

_____

Ask the Lord to bless these people today.

KEEP communicating with God today

Promptings from the Spirit   **Blessings I received today**

_____   _____

_____   _____

_____   _____

_____   _____

_____   _____

Be grateful, be smart, be clean, be true, be humble, be prayerful.
Gordon B Hinckley

My TALK with God today   **Day**   **Date**

☐ Morning Prayer   ☐ Evening Prayer

ASK IN FAITH

Three Things I am **THANKFUL** for Today:

1.

2.

3.

Turn this over to the Lord. **LET** go and let God handle it

What do I need forgiveness for?

Ask God to help with this challenge today.

Prayer with action makes a difference. I set these intentions for the day:

_____

_____

_____

_____

_____

Ask the Lord to bless these people today.

KEEP communicating with God today

Promptings from the Spirit   Blessings I received today

_____   _____

_____   _____

_____   _____

_____   _____

_____   _____

Be kind, and be grateful that God is kind. It is a happy way to live.
Jeffrey R. Holland

My TALK with God today   **Day**   **Date**

| ☐ **Morning Prayer** | ☐ **Evening Prayer** | **ASK IN FAITH** |

Three Things I am **THANKFUL** for Today:

What do I need forgiveness for?

1.

2.

3.

Turn this over to the Lord. **LET** go and let God handle it

Ask God to help with this challenge today.

Prayer with action makes a difference. I set these intentions for the day:

_____

_____

Ask the Lord to bless these people today.

_____

_____

_____

KEEP communicating with God today

Promptings from the Spirit   **Blessings I received today**

_____   _____

_____   _____

_____   _____

_____   _____

_____   _____

Arise, shine; for thy light is come, and the glory of the Lord is risen upon thee.
Isaiah 60:1

My TALK with God today | **Day** | **Date**

❑ Morning Prayer	❑ Evening Prayer

ASK IN FAITH

Three Things I am **THANKFUL** for Today:

1.

2.

3.

Turn this over to the Lord. **LET** go and let God handle it

What do I need forgiveness for?

Ask God to help with this challenge today.

Prayer with action makes a difference. I set these intentions for the day:

_____

_____

_____

_____

_____

Ask the Lord to bless these people today.

KEEP communicating with God today

Promptings from the Spirit

_____

_____

_____

_____

_____

Blessings I received today

_____

_____

_____

_____

_____

Be not deceived; God is not mocked: for whatsoever a man soweth, that shall he also reap.
Galatians 6:7

My TALK with God today **Day** **Date**

☐ Morning Prayer	☐ Evening Prayer

ASK IN FAITH

Three Things I am **THANKFUL** for Today:
1.
2.
3.

What do I need forgiveness for?

Turn this over to the Lord. **LET** go and let God handle it

Ask God to help with this challenge today.

Prayer with action makes a difference. I set these intentions for the day:

_____
_____
_____
_____
_____

Ask the Lord to bless these people today.

KEEP communicating with God today

Promptings from the Spirit	Blessings I received today
_____	_____
_____	_____
_____	_____
_____	_____
_____	_____

Be patient with yourself. Self-growth is tender; it's holy ground. There's no greater investment.
Steven R Covey

My TALK with God today **Day** | **Date**

☐ Morning Prayer ☐ Evening Prayer | **ASK IN FAITH**

Three Things I am **THANKFUL** for Today: | **What do I need forgiveness for?**

1.

2.

3.

Turn this over to the Lord. **LET** go and let God handle it | Ask God to help with this challenge today.

Prayer with action makes a difference. I set these intentions for the day:

_____

_____

_____ | Ask the Lord to bless these people today.

_____

_____

KEEP communicating with God today

Promptings from the Spirit   Blessings I received today

_____   _____

_____   _____ | Be strong in the grace that is in Christ Jesus. 2 Timothy 2:1

_____   _____

_____   _____

_____   _____

My TALK with God today   Day   Date

| ☐ Morning Prayer | ☐ Evening Prayer | **ASK IN FAITH** |

Three Things I am THANKFUL for Today:

1.

2.

3.

Turn this over to the Lord. **LET** go and let God handle it

Prayer with action makes a difference. I set these intentions for the day:

_____

_____

_____

_____

_____

What do I need forgiveness for?

Ask God to help with this challenge today.

Ask the Lord to bless these people today.

KEEP communicating with God today

Promptings from the Spirit   Blessings I received today

_____   _____

_____   _____

_____   _____

_____   _____

_____   _____

Be of good cheer, for I will lead you along. The kingdom is yours and the blessings thereof are yours, and the riches of eternity are yours..
D&C 78:18

My TALK with God today **Day** **Date**

☐ **Morning Prayer** ☐ **Evening Prayer**

Three Things I am **THANKFUL** for Today:
1.
2.
3.

Turn this over to the Lord. **LET** go and let God handle it

Prayer with action makes a difference. I set these intentions for the day:

_____

_____

_____

_____

_____

KEEP communicating with God today

Promptings from the Spirit **Blessings I received today**

_____ _____

_____ _____

_____ _____

_____ _____

_____ _____

ASK IN FAITH

What do I need forgiveness for?

Ask God to help with this challenge today.

Ask the Lord to bless these people today.

Be ye doers of the word, and not hearers only, deceiving your own selves
James 1:22

My TALK with God today   **Day**   **Date**

☐ Morning Prayer	☐ Evening Prayer

ASK IN FAITH

Three Things I am **THANKFUL** for Today:
1.
2.
3.

What do I need forgiveness for?

Turn this over to the Lord. **LET** go and let God handle it

Ask God to help with this challenge today.

Prayer with action makes a difference. I set these intentions for the day:

_____

_____

_____

_____

_____

Ask the Lord to bless these people today.

KEEP communicating with God today

Promptings from the Spirit	Blessings I received today
_____	_____
_____	_____
_____	_____
_____	_____
_____	_____

Behold I say unto you that he cannot have faith and hope, save he shall be meek, and lowly of heart. Moroni 7:43

My TALK with God today → **Day** **Date**

| ☐ Morning Prayer | ☐ Evening Prayer | **ASK IN FAITH** |

Three Things I am **THANKFUL** for Today:

What do I need forgiveness for?

1.

2.

3.

I turn this over to the Lord. **LET** go and let God handle it

Ask God to help with this challenge today.

Prayer with action makes a difference. I set these intentions for the day:

_____

_____

_____

_____

_____

Ask the Lord to bless these people today..

KEEP communicating with God today

Promptings from the Spirit   **Blessings I received today**

_____   _____

_____   _____

_____   _____

_____   _____

_____   _____

Being enriched in every thing to all bountifulness, which causeth through us thanksgiving to God. 2 Corinthians 9:11

My TALK with God today **Day** **Date**

| ☐ Morning Prayer | ☐ Evening Prayer | **ASK IN FAITH** |

Three Things I am **THANKFUL** for Today:

1.

2.

3.

I turn this over to the Lord. **LET** go and let God handle it

Prayer with action makes a difference. I set these intentions for the day:

_____

_____

_____

_____

_____

KEEP communicating with God today

Promptings from the Spirit

_____

_____

_____

_____

_____

Blessings I received today

_____

_____

_____

_____

_____

What do I need forgiveness for?

Ask God to help with this challenge today.

Ask the Lord to bless these people today..

Believe in prophesying, and in revelations, and in the ministering of angels, and in the gift of tongues...and in all things which are good.
Omni 1:25

My TALK with God today   **Day**   **Date**

☐   **Morning Prayer**   ☐   **Evening Prayer**

ASK IN FAITH

Three Things I am **THANKFUL** for Today:

1.

2.

3.

What do I need forgiveness for?

I turn this over to the Lord. **LET** go and let God handle it

Ask God to help with this challenge today.

Prayer with action makes a difference. I set these intentions for the day:

_____

_____

_____

_____

_____

Ask the Lord to bless these people today..

KEEP communicating with God today

Promptings from the Spirit   Blessings I received today

_____ _____

_____ _____

_____ _____

_____ _____

_____ _____

Bless them which persecute you: bless, and curse not.
Romans 12:14

My TALK with God today

Day

Date

☐ Morning Prayer	☐ Evening Prayer

ASK IN FAITH

Three Things I am **THANKFUL** for Today:

What do I need forgiveness for?

1.

2.

3.

I turn this over to the Lord. **LET** go and let God handle it

Ask God to help with this challenge today.

Prayer with action makes a difference. I set these intentions for the day:

_____

_____

Ask the Lord to bless these people today..

_____

_____

_____

KEEP communicating with God today

Promptings from the Spirit   **Blessings I received today**

_____   _____

_____   _____

_____   _____

_____   _____

_____   _____

Blessed are the pure in heart: for they shall see God. Matthew 5:8

My TALK with God today

Day

Date

☐ Morning Prayer   ☐ Evening Prayer

ASK IN FAITH

Three Things I am **THANKFUL** for Today:

1.

2.

3.

What do I need forgiveness for?

I turn this over to the Lord. **LET** go and let God handle it

Ask God to help with this challenge today.

Prayer with action makes a difference. I set these intentions for the day:

_____
_____
_____
_____
_____

Ask the Lord to bless these people today..

KEEP communicating with God today

Promptings from the Spirit   Blessings I received today
_____   _____
_____   _____
_____   _____
_____   _____
_____   _____

Blessed are they that have not seen, and yet have believed.
John 20:29

My TALK with God today **Day** **Date**

☐ Morning Prayer ☐ Evening Prayer

ASK IN FAITH

Three Things I am **THANKFUL** for Today:

1.

2.

3.

I turn this over to the Lord. **LET** go and let God handle it

What do I need forgiveness for?

Ask God to help with this challenge today.

Prayer with action makes a difference. I set these intentions for the day:

_____

_____

._____

_____

_____

Ask the Lord to bless these people today..

KEEP communicating with God today

Promptings from the Spirit   Blessings I received today

_____ _____

_____ _____

_____ _____

_____ _____

_____ _____

Blessed are they which do hunger and thirst after righteousness: for they shall be filled.
Matthew 5:6

My TALK with God today | **Day** | **Date**

☐ Morning Prayer	☐ Evening Prayer

ASK IN FAITH

Three Things I am **THANKFUL** for Today:

1.

2.

3.

I turn this over to the Lord. **LET** go and let God handle it

What do I need forgiveness for?

Ask God to help with this challenge today.

Prayer with action makes a difference. I set these intentions for the day:

_____

_____

_____

_____

_____

Ask the Lord to bless these people today..

KEEP communicating with God today

Promptings from the Spirit | Blessings I received today

_____ | _____

_____ | _____

_____ | _____

_____ | _____

_____ | _____

Blessed are those who mourn, for they will be comforted.
Matthew 5:4

My TALK with God today **Day** **Date**

☐ Morning Prayer	☐ Evening Prayer

ASK IN FAITH

Three Things I am **THANKFUL** for Today:

1.

2.

3.

What do I need forgiveness for?

I turn this over to the Lord. **LET** go and let God handle it

Ask God to help with this challenge today.

Prayer with action makes a difference. I set these intentions for the day:

_____

_____

_____

_____

_____

Ask the Lord to bless these people today..

KEEP communicating with God today

Promptings from the Spirit

_____

_____

_____

_____

_____

Blessings I received today

_____

_____

_____

_____

_____

Blessed is the man that endureth temptation: for when he is tried, he shall receive the crown of life, which the Lord hath promised to them that love him.
James 1:12

My TALK with God today → **Day** | **Date**

☐ **Morning Prayer** | ☐ **Evening Prayer**

Three Things I am **THANKFUL** for Today:

1.

2.

3.

I turn this over to the Lord. **LET** go and let God handle it

What do I need forgiveness for?

Ask God to help with this challenge today.

Prayer with action makes a difference. I set these intentions for the day:

_____

_____

_____

_____

_____

Ask the Lord to bless these people today..

KEEP communicating with God today

Promptings from the Spirit | Blessings I received today

_____ | _____

_____ | _____

_____ | _____

_____ | _____

_____ | _____

But behold, all things have been done in the wisdom of him who knoweth all things.
2 Nephi 2:24

My TALK with God today ➡ Day   Date

☐ Morning Prayer	☐ Evening Prayer

ASK IN FAITH

Three Things I am THANKFUL for Today:

1.

2.

3.

I turn this over to the Lord. **LET** go and let God handle it

What do I need forgiveness for?

Ask God to help with this challenge today.

Prayer with action makes a difference. I set these intentions for the day:

_____

_____

_____

_____

_____

Ask the Lord to bless these people today.

KEEP communicating with God today

Promptings from the Spirit	Blessings I received today
_____	_____
_____	_____
_____	_____
_____	_____
_____	

But charity is the pure love of Christ, and it endureth forever; and whoso is found possessed of it at the last day, it shall be well with him.
Moroni 7:47

My TALK with God today ➤ **Day** | **Date**

☐ Morning Prayer	☐ Evening Prayer

ASK IN FAITH

Three Things I am **THANKFUL** for Today:

1.

2.

3.

What do I need forgiveness for?

I turn this over to the Lord. **LET** go and let God handle it

Ask God to help with this challenge today.

Prayer with action makes a difference. I set these intentions for the day:

_____

_____

_____

Ask the Lord to bless these people today.

_____

_____

KEEP communicating with God today

Promptings from the Spirit | Blessings I received today
_____ _____
_____ _____
_____ _____
_____ _____
_____ _____

But godliness with contentment is great gain.
1 Timothy 6:6

My TALK with God today   **Day**   **Date**

☐ Morning Prayer	☐ Evening Prayer	**ASK IN FAITH**

Three Things I am **THANKFUL** for Today:

What do I need forgiveness for?

1.

2.

3.

I turn this over to the Lord. **LET** go and let God handle it

Ask God to help with this challenge today.

Prayer with action makes a difference. I set these intentions for the day:

_____

_____

_____

_____

_____

Ask the Lord to bless these people today.

KEEP communicating with God today

Promptings from the Spirit   **Blessings I received today**

_____   _____

_____   _____

_____   _____

_____   _____

_____   _____

But grow in grace, and in the knowledge of our Lord and Savior Jesus Christ. To him be glory both now and for ever.
2 Peter 3:18

My TALK with God today → **Day** **Date**

☐ Morning Prayer	☐ Evening Prayer

ASK IN FAITH

Three Things I am **THANKFUL** for Today:

1.

2.

3.

What do I need forgiveness for?

I turn this over to the Lord. **LET** go and let God handle it

Ask God to help with this challenge today.

Prayer with action makes a difference. I set these intentions for the day:

_____

_____

_____

_____

_____

Ask the Lord to bless these people today.

KEEP communicating with God today

Promptings from the Spirit

_____

_____

_____

_____

_____

Blessings I received today

_____

_____

_____

_____

_____

But he that shall endure unto the end, the same shall be saved.
Matthew 24:13

My TALK with God today | **Day** | **Date**

☐ Morning Prayer ☐ Evening Prayer

Three Things I am **THANKFUL** for Today:

1.

2.

3.

I turn this over to the Lord. **LET** go and let God handle it

Prayer with action makes a difference. I set these intentions for the day:

_____

_____

_____

_____

_____

KEEP communicating with God today

Promptings from the Spirit   Blessings I received today

_____   _____

_____   _____

_____   _____

_____   _____

_____   _____

ASK IN FAITH

What do I need forgiveness for?

Ask God to help with this challenge today.

Ask the Lord to bless these people today.

But let him ask in faith, nothing wavering.
James 1:6

My TALK with God today | Day | Date

☐ Morning Prayer   ☐ Evening Prayer

ASK IN FAITH

Three Things I am **THANKFUL** for Today:

1.

2.

3.

I turn this over to the Lord. **LET** go and let God handle it

What do I need forgiveness for?

Ask God to help with this challenge today.

Prayer with action makes a difference. I set these intentions for the day:

_____
_____
_____
_____
_____

Ask the Lord to bless these people today.

KEEP communicating with God today

Promptings from the Spirit   **Blessings I received today**

_____   _____
_____   _____
_____   _____
_____   _____
_____   _____

But love ye your enemies, and do good, and lend, hoping for nothing again; and your reward shall be great.
Luke 6:35

My TALK with God today ➤ **Day** **Date**

☐ Morning Prayer	☐ Evening Prayer	**ASK IN FAITH**

Three Things I am **THANKFUL** for Today:

1.

2.

3.

What do I need forgiveness for?

I turn this over to the Lord. **LET** go and let God handle it

Ask God to help with this challenge today.

Prayer with action makes a difference. I set these intentions for the day:

_____

_____

_____

_____

_____

Ask the Lord to bless these people today.

KEEP communicating with God today

Promptings from the Spirit   **Blessings I received today**

_____   _____

_____   _____

_____   _____

_____   _____

_____   _____

But that ye would humble yourselves before the Lord, and call on his holy name, and watch and pray continually, that ye may not be tempted above that which ye can bear.
Alma 13:28

My TALK with God today →	Day		Date

☐ Morning Prayer	☐ Evening Prayer	**ASK IN FAITH**

Three Things I am **THANKFUL** for Today:	**What do I need forgiveness for?**
1.	
2.	
3.	

I turn this over to the Lord. **LET** go and let God handle it

Ask God to help with this challenge today.

Prayer with action makes a difference. I set these intentions for the day:

_____

_____

Ask the Lord to bless these people today.

_____

_____

_____

KEEP communicating with God today

Promptings from the Spirit	Blessings I received today
_____	_____
_____	_____
_____	_____
_____	_____
_____	_____

But the fruit of the Spirit is love, joy, peace, longsuffering, gentleness, goodness, faith, Meekness, temperance: against such there is no law. Galatians 5:22-23

My TALK with God today → Day   Date

☐ Morning Prayer	☐ Evening Prayer

ASK IN FAITH

Three Things I am **THANKFUL** for Today:

1.

2.

3.

I turn this over to the Lord. **LET** go and let God handle it

Prayer with action makes a difference. I set these intentions for the day:

_____
_____
_____
_____
_____

What do I need forgiveness for?

Ask God to help with this challenge today.

Ask the Lord to bless these people today.

KEEP communicating with God today

Promptings from the Spirit	Blessings I received today
_____	_____
_____	_____
_____	_____
_____	_____
_____	_____

But the human spirit is resilient. God made us so. He gave us the ability to forgive. To leave our past behind. To look forward instead of back.
Elizabeth Smart

My TALK with God today → Day

Date

☐ **Morning Prayer** ☐ **Evening Prayer**

ASK IN FAITH

What do I need forgiveness for?

Three Things I am **THANKFUL** for Today:

1.

2.

3.

I turn this over to the Lord. **LET** go and let God handle it

Ask God to help with this challenge today.

Prayer with action makes a difference. I set these intentions for the day:

_____

_____

_____

_____

_____

Ask the Lord to bless these people today.

KEEP communicating with God today

Promptings from the Spirit

_____

_____

_____

_____

_____

Blessings I received today

_____

_____

_____

_____

But they that wait upon the Lord shall renew their strength; they shall mount up with wings as eagles; they shall run, and not be weary; and they shall walk, and not faint.
Isiah 40:31

My TALK with God today   **Day**   **Date**

☐ Morning Prayer	☐ Evening Prayer

ASK IN FAITH

Three Things I am **THANKFUL** for Today:

1.

2.

3.

I turn this over to the Lord. **LET** go and let God handle it

What do I need
forgiveness for?

Ask God to help with this
challenge today.

Prayer with action makes a difference. I set these intentions for the day:

_____

_____

_____

_____

_____

Ask the Lord to bless
these people today.

KEEP communicating with God today

Promptings from the Spirit   Blessings I received today

_____   _____

_____   _____

_____   _____

_____   _____

_____   _____

But when the
Comforter is come,
whom I will send unto
you from the Father,
even the Spirit of truth,
which proceedeth from
the Father, he shall
testify of me.
John 15:26

My TALK with God today   **Day**   **Date**

☐ **Morning Prayer**   ☐ **Evening Prayer**   **ASK IN FAITH**

Three Things I am **THANKFUL** for Today:
1.
2.
3.

What do I need forgiveness for?

I turn this over to the Lord. **LET** go and let God handle it

Ask God to help with this challenge today.

Prayer with action makes a difference. I set these intentions for the day:

_____

_____

_____

_____

_____

Ask the Lord to bless these people today.

KEEP communicating with God today

Promptings from the Spirit   **Blessings I received today**

_____ _____

_____ _____

_____ _____

_____ _____

_____ _____

But wo, wo unto him who knoweth that he rebelleth against God! For salvation cometh to none such except it be through repentance and faith on the Lord Jesus Christ
Mosiah 3:12

My TALK with God today → **Day**   **Date**

☐ Morning Prayer	☐ Evening Prayer

ASK IN FAITH

Three Things I am **THANKFUL** for Today:
1.
2.
3.

I turn this over to the Lord. **LET** go and let God handle it

What do I need forgiveness for?

Ask God to help with this challenge today.

Prayer with action makes a difference. I set these intentions for the day:

_____

_____

_____

_____

_____

Ask the Lord to bless these people today.

KEEP communicating with God today

Promptings from the Spirit	Blessings I received today
_____	_____
_____	_____
_____	_____
_____	_____
_____	_____

But ye are commanded in all things to ask of God, who giveth liberally. D&C 46:7

My TALK with God today   **Day**   **Date**

❏ Morning Prayer	❏ Evening Prayer

ASK IN FAITH

What do I need forgiveness for?

Three Things I am **THANKFUL** for Today:
1.
2.
3.

I turn this over to the Lord. **LET** go and let God handle it

Ask God to help with this challenge today.

Prayer with action makes a difference. I set these intentions for the day:

_____

_____

_____

_____

_____

Ask the Lord to bless these people today.

KEEP communicating with God today

Promptings from the Spirit	Blessings I received today
_____	_____
_____	_____
_____	_____
_____	_____
_____	_____

But ye will teach them to walk in the ways of truth and soberness; ye will teach them to love one another, and to serve one another.
Mosiah 4:15

My TALK with God today → **Day**   **Date**

☐ Morning Prayer	☐ Evening Prayer

ASK IN FAITH

Three Things I am **THANKFUL** for Today:
1.
2.
3.

What do I need forgiveness for?

I turn this over to the Lord. **LET** go and let God handle it

Ask God to help with this challenge today.

Prayer with action makes a difference. I set these intentions for the day:

_____

_____

_____

_____

_____

Ask the Lord to bless these people today.

KEEP communicating with God today

Promptings from the Spirit	Blessings I received today
_____	_____
_____	_____
_____	_____
_____	_____
_____	_____

By this shall all men know that ye are my disciples, if ye have love one to another.
John 13:35

My TALK with God today **Day** **Date**

| ☐ Morning Prayer | ☐ Evening Prayer | **ASK IN FAITH** |

Three Things I am **THANKFUL** for Today:

What do I need forgiveness for?

1.

2.

3.

I turn this over to the Lord. **LET** go and let God handle it

Ask God to help with this challenge today.

Prayer with action makes a difference. I set these intentions for the day:

_____

_____

_____

_____

_____

Ask the Lord to bless these people today.

KEEP communicating with God today

| Promptings from the Spirit | Blessings I received today |

_____ _____

_____ _____

_____ _____

_____ _____

_____ _____

Call on his name in faith, believing that ye shall receive, then shalt thou receive the hope which thou desirest.
Alma 22:16

My TALK with God today → **Day**   **Date**

☐ **Morning Prayer**   ☐ **Evening Prayer**   **ASK IN FAITH**

Three Things I am **THANKFUL** for Today:
1.
2.
3.

I turn this over to the Lord. **LET** go and let God handle it

What do I need forgiveness for?

Ask God to help with this challenge today.

Prayer with action makes a difference. I set these intentions for the day:

_____

_____

_____

_____

_____

Ask the Lord to bless these people today.

KEEP communicating with God today

Promptings from the Spirit   Blessings I received today

_____   _____

_____   _____

_____   _____

_____   _____

_____   _____

Casting all your care upon him; for he careth for you.
1 Peter 5:7

My TALK with God today   **Day**   **Date**

☐ **Morning Prayer**	☐ **Evening Prayer**	**ASK IN FAITH**

Three Things I am **THANKFUL** for Today:
1.
2.
3.

What do I need forgiveness for?

I turn this over to the Lord. **LET** go and let God handle it

Ask God to help with this challenge today.

Prayer with action makes a difference. I set these intentions for the day:

_____

_____

_____

_____

_____

Ask the Lord to bless these people today.

KEEP communicating with God today

Promptings from the Spirit	**Blessings I received today**
_____	_____
_____	_____
_____	_____
_____	_____
_____	_____

Character is determined by the extent to which we can master ourselves toward good ends.
N Eldon Tanner

My TALK with God today → Day   Date

☐ **Morning Prayer**   ☐ **Evening Prayer**

ASK IN FAITH

Three Things I am **THANKFUL** for Today:

1.

2.

3.

Turn this over to the Lord. **LET** go and let God handle it

What do I need forgiveness for?

Ask God to help with this challenge today.

Prayer with action makes a difference. I set these intentions for the day:

_____

_____

_____

_____

_____

Ask the Lord to bless these people today.

KEEP communicating with God today

Promptings from the Spirit   Blessings I received today

_____   _____

_____   _____

_____   _____

_____   _____

_____   _____

Character, simply stated, is doing what you say you're going to do.
Hyrum W Smith

My TALK with God today → Day

Date

☐ **Morning Prayer**   ☐ **Evening Prayer**

ASK IN FAITH

Three Things I am **THANKFUL** for Today:

1.

2.

3.

What do I need forgiveness for?

Turn this over to the Lord. **LET** go and let God handle it

Ask God to help with this challenge today.

Prayer with action makes a difference. I set these intentions for the day:

_____

_____

_____

_____

_____

Ask the Lord to bless these people today.

KEEP communicating with God today

Promptings from the Spirit   Blessings I received today

_____   _____

_____   _____

_____   _____

_____   _____

_____   _____

Choose you this day whom ye will serve; as for me and my house, we will serve the Lord. Joshua 24:15

My TALK with God today   **Day**   **Date**

❑ Morning Prayer	❑ Evening Prayer	**ASK IN FAITH**

Three Things I am **THANKFUL** for Today:

What do I need forgiveness for?

1.

2.

3.

Turn this over to the Lord. **LET** go and let God handle it

Ask God to help with this challenge today.

Prayer with action makes a difference. I set these intentions for the day:

_____

_____

_____

_____

_____

Ask the Lord to bless these people today.

KEEP communicating with God today

Promptings from the Spirit	Blessings I received today
_____	_____
_____	_____
_____	_____
_____	_____
_____	_____

Come unto me, all ye that labor and are heavy laden, and I will give you rest.
Matthew 11:28

My TALK with God today → **Day**   **Date**

☐ **Morning Prayer**   ☐ **Evening Prayer**

ASK IN FAITH

Three Things I am **THANKFUL** for Today:

1.

2.

3.

Turn this over to the Lord. **LET** go and let God handle it

What do I need forgiveness for?

Ask God to help with this challenge today.

Prayer with action makes a difference. I set these intentions for the day:

_____

_____

_____

_____

_____

Ask the Lord to bless these people today.

KEEP communicating with God today

Promptings from the Spirit   **Blessings I received today**

_____   _____

_____   _____

_____   _____

_____   _____

_____   _____

Coveting, pouting, or tearing others down does not elevate your standing, nor does demeaning someone else improve your self-image.
Jeffrey R. Holland

My TALK with God today **Day** **Date**

☐ Morning Prayer	☐ Evening Prayer

ASK IN FAITH

What do I need forgiveness for?

Three Things I am **THANKFUL** for Today:

1.

2.

3.

Turn this over to the Lord. **LET** go and let God handle it

Ask God to help with this challenge today.

Prayer with action makes a difference. I set these intentions for the day:

_____

_____

_____

_____

_____

Ask the Lord to bless these people today.

KEEP communicating with God today

Promptings from the Spirit	Blessings I received today
_____	_____
_____	_____
_____	_____
_____	_____
_____	_____

Daily hope is vital, since the 'Winter Quarters' of our lives are not immediately adjacent to our promised land either. An arduous trek still awaits, but hope spurs weary disciples on.
Neal A. Maxwell

My TALK with God today	Day		Date

☐ Morning Prayer	☐ Evening Prayer

ASK IN FAITH

Three Things I am **THANKFUL** for Today:
1.
2.
3.

What do I need forgiveness for?

Turn this over to the Lord. **LET** go and let God handle it

Ask God to help with this challenge today.

Prayer with action makes a difference. I set these intentions for the day:

_____
_____
_____
_____
_____

Ask the Lord to bless these people today.

KEEP communicating with God today

Promptings from the Spirit	Blessings I received today
_____	_____
_____	_____
_____	_____
_____	_____
_____	_____

Devote yourselves to prayer, being watchful and thankful.
Colossians 4:2

My TALK with God today	Day	Date

☐ Morning Prayer	☐ Evening Prayer

ASK IN FAITH

Three Things I am **THANKFUL** for Today:

1.

2.

3.

Turn this over to the Lord. **LET** go and let God handle it

What do I need forgiveness for?

Ask God to help with this challenge today.

Prayer with action makes a difference. I set these intentions for the day:

_____

_____

_____

_____

_____

Ask the Lord to bless these people today.

KEEP communicating with God today

Promptings from the Spirit	Blessings I received today
_____	_____
_____	_____
_____	_____
_____	_____
_____	_____

Discouragement is not the absence of adequacy but the absence of courage.
Neal A. Maxwell

My TALK with God today **Day** **Date**

☐ **Morning Prayer**   ☐ **Evening Prayer**

ASK IN FAITH

Three Things I am **THANKFUL** for Today:

1.

2.

3.

Turn this over to the Lord. **LET** go and let God handle it

What do I need forgiveness for?

Ask God to help with this challenge today.

Prayer with action makes a difference. I set these intentions for the day:

_____

_____

_____

_____

_____

Ask the Lord to bless these people today.

KEEP communicating with God today

Promptings from the Spirit   **Blessings I received today**

_____   _____

_____   _____

_____   _____

_____   _____

_____   _____

Do not be anxious about anything, but in every situation, by prayer and petition, with thanksgiving, present your requests to God. And the peace of God, which transcends all understanding, will guard your hearts and your minds in Christ Jesus.
Philippians 4:6-7

My TALK with God today   **Day**   **Date**

☐ Morning Prayer	☐ Evening Prayer	**ASK IN FAITH**

Three Things I am **THANKFUL** for Today:

1.

2.

3.

What do I need forgiveness for?

Turn this over to the Lord. **LET** go and let God handle it

Ask God to help with this challenge today.

Prayer with action makes a difference. I set these intentions for the day:

_____

_____

_____

_____

_____

Ask the Lord to bless these people today.

KEEP communicating with God today

Promptings from the Spirit	Blessings I received today
_____	_____
_____	_____
_____	_____
_____	_____
_____	_____

Every good gift and every perfect gift is from above, and cometh down from the Father.
James 1:17

My TALK with God today → **Day** _____ **Date** _____

☐ Morning Prayer ☐ Evening Prayer

ASK IN FAITH

Three Things I am **THANKFUL** for Today:

1.

2.

3.

What do I need forgiveness for?

I turn this over to the Lord. **LET** go and let God handle it

Ask God to help with this challenge today.

Prayer with action makes a difference. I set these intentions for the day:

_____

_____

_____

_____

_____

Ask the Lord to bless these people today..

KEEP communicating with God today

Promptings from the Spirit   Blessings I received today

_____   _____

_____   _____

_____   _____

_____   _____

_____   _____

Everyone would like to have stronger faith. By themselves, the scriptures may not strengthen your faith, but being faithful to what they teach, does. In other words, faith cannot be separated from faithfulness.
John Bytheway

My TALK with God today   **Day**   **Date**

☐ Morning Prayer	☐ Evening Prayer

ASK IN FAITH

Three Things I am **THANKFUL** for Today:

1.

2.

3.

I turn this over to the Lord. **LET** go and let God handle it

What do I need forgiveness for?

Ask God to help with this challenge today.

Prayer with action makes a difference. I set these intentions for the day:

_____

_____

_____

_____

_____

Ask the Lord to bless these people today..

KEEP communicating with God today

Promptings from the Spirit   Blessings I received today

_____   _____

_____   _____

_____   _____

_____   _____

_____   _____

Except ye be converted, and become as little children, ye shall not enter into the kingdom of heaven. Matthew 18:3

My TALK with God today **Day** **Date**

☐ Morning Prayer	☐ Evening Prayer

Three Things I am **THANKFUL** for Today:

1.

2.

3.

I turn this over to the Lord. **LET** go and let God handle it

What do I need forgiveness for?

Ask God to help with this challenge today.

Prayer with action makes a difference. I set these intentions for the day:

_____

_____

_____

_____

_____

Ask the Lord to bless these people today..

KEEP communicating with God today

Promptings from the Spirit	Blessings I received today
_____	_____
_____	_____
_____	_____
_____	_____
_____	_____

Exercising faith in Christ is trusting and placing our confidence in Him as our Savior, on His name, and in His promises.
David A Bednar

My TALK with God today **Day** **Date**

| ☐ Morning Prayer | ☐ Evening Prayer | **ASK IN FAITH** |

Three Things I am **THANKFUL** for Today:

1.

2.

3.

What do I need forgiveness for?

I turn this over to the Lord. **LET** go and let God handle it

Ask God to help with this challenge today.

Prayer with action makes a difference. I set these intentions for the day:

_____

_____

_____

_____

_____

Ask the Lord to bless these people today..

KEEP communicating with God today

Promptings from the Spirit   Blessings I received today

_____   _____

_____   _____

_____   _____

_____   _____

_____   _____

Faith and repentance bringeth a change of heart.
Helaman 15:7

My TALK with God today	Day	Date

☐ Morning Prayer	☐ Evening Prayer	**ASK IN FAITH**

Three Things I am **THANKFUL** for Today:	**What do I need forgiveness for?**
1.	
2.	
3.	

I turn this over to the Lord. **LET** go and let God handle it	**Ask God to help with this challenge today.**

Prayer with action makes a difference. I set these intentions for the day:

Ask the Lord to bless these people today..

_____

_____

_____

_____

_____

KEEP communicating with God today

Promptings from the Spirit	Blessings I received today
_____	_____
_____	_____
_____	_____
_____	_____
_____	_____

Faith is not so much something we believe; faith is something we live.
Joseph B. Wirthlin

My TALK with God today | **Day** | **Date**

☐ Morning Prayer	☐ Evening Prayer

ASK IN FAITH

Three Things I am **THANKFUL** for Today:

1.

2.

3.

What do I need forgiveness for?

I turn this over to the Lord. **LET** go and let God handle it

Ask God to help with this challenge today.

Prayer with action makes a difference. I set these intentions for the day:

_____

_____

_____

_____

_____

Ask the Lord to bless these people today..

KEEP communicating with God today

Promptings from the Spirit | Blessings I received today

_____ _____

_____ _____

_____ _____

_____ _____

_____ _____

Fear not: for I have redeemed thee, I have called thee by thy name; thou art mine.
Isaiah 43:1

My TALK with God today

Day

Date

☐ Morning Prayer   ☐ Evening Prayer

ASK IN FAITH

Three Things I am **THANKFUL** for Today:

1.

2.

3.

What do I need forgiveness for?

I turn this over to the Lord. **LET** go and let God handle it

Ask God to help with this challenge today.

Prayer with action makes a difference. I set these intentions for the day:

_____

_____

_____

_____

_____

Ask the Lord to bless these people today..

KEEP communicating with God today

Promptings from the Spirit

_____

_____

_____

_____

_____

Blessings I received today

_____

_____

_____

_____

_____

Fear thou not; for I am with thee: be not dismayed; for I am thy God: I will strengthen thee; yea, I will help thee; yea, I will uphold thee with the right hand of my righteousness. Isaiah 41:10

My TALK with God today	Day	Date

☐ Morning Prayer	☐ Evening Prayer

ASK IN FAITH

Three Things I am **THANKFUL** for Today:

1.

2.

3.

I turn this over to the Lord. **LET** go and let God handle it

What do I need forgiveness for?

Prayer with action makes a difference. I set these intentions for the day:

_____

_____

_____

_____

_____

Ask God to help with this challenge today.

Ask the Lord to bless these people today..

KEEP communicating with God today

Promptings from the Spirit	Blessings I received today
_____	_____
_____	_____
_____	_____
_____	_____
_____	_____

Finally, be ye all of one mind, having compassion one of another, love as brethren, be pitiful, be courteous.
1 Peter 3:8

My TALK with God today ➤ **Day** **Date**

☐ Morning Prayer	☐ Evening Prayer

ASK IN FAITH

Three Things I am **THANKFUL** for Today:

1.

2.

3.

I turn this over to the Lord. **LET** go and let God handle it

What do I need forgiveness for?

Ask God to help with this challenge today.

Prayer with action makes a difference. I set these intentions for the day:

_____

_____

_____

_____

_____

Ask the Lord to bless these people today..

KEEP communicating with God today

Promptings from the Spirit	Blessings I received today
_____	_____
_____	_____
_____	_____
_____	_____
_____	_____

For as many as are led by the Spirit of God, they are the sons of God.
Romans 8:14

My TALK with God today → Day _____   Date _____

☐ Morning Prayer	☐ Evening Prayer

ASK IN FAITH

Three Things I am **THANKFUL** for Today:

What do I need forgiveness for?

1.

2.

3.

I turn this over to the Lord. **LET** go and let God handle it

Ask God to help with this challenge today.

Prayer with action makes a difference. I set these intentions for the day:

_____

_____

Ask the Lord to bless these people today.

_____

_____

_____

KEEP communicating with God today

Promptings from the Spirit   **Blessings I received today**

_____   _____

_____   _____

_____   _____

_____   _____

_____   _____

For behold, I am God; and I am a God of miracles; and I will show unto the world that I am the same yesterday, today, and forever.
2 Nephi 27:23

My TALK with God today ➤ **Day**   **Date**

☐ Morning Prayer	☐ Evening Prayer

ASK IN FAITH

Three Things I am **THANKFUL** for Today:

1.

2.

3.

What do I need forgiveness for?

I turn this over to the Lord. **LET** go and let God handle it

Ask God to help with this challenge today.

Prayer with action makes a difference. I set these intentions for the day:

_____

_____

_____

_____

_____

Ask the Lord to bless these people today.

KEEP communicating with God today

Promptings from the Spirit	Blessings I received today
_____	_____
_____	_____
_____	_____
_____	_____
_____	_____

For by grace are ye saved through faith; and that not of yourselves: it is the gift of God.
Ephesians 2:8

My TALK with God today → **Day**   **Date**

☐ Morning Prayer	☐ Evening Prayer	**ASK IN FAITH**

What do I need forgiveness for?

Three Things I am **THANKFUL** for Today:

1.

2.

3.

I turn this over to the Lord. **LET** go and let God handle it

Ask God to help with this challenge today.

Prayer with action makes a difference. I set these intentions for the day:

_____

_____

_____

_____

_____

Ask the Lord to bless these people today.

KEEP communicating with God today

Promptings from the Spirit	Blessings I received today
_____	_____
_____	_____
_____	_____
_____	_____
_____	_____

For David speaketh concerning him, I foresaw the Lord always before my face, for he is on my right hand, that I should not be moved.
Acts 2:25

My TALK with God today ➤ **Day**   **Date**

☐ Morning Prayer	☐ Evening Prayer

ASK IN FAITH

Three Things I am **THANKFUL** for Today:

1.

2.

3.

I turn this over to the Lord. **LET** go and let God handle it

What do I need forgiveness for?

Ask God to help with this challenge today.

Prayer with action makes a difference. I set these intentions for the day:

_____

_____

_____

_____

_____

Ask the Lord to bless these people today.

KEEP communicating with God today

Promptings from the Spirit   Blessings I received today

_____   _____

_____   _____

_____   _____

_____   _____

_____   _____

For He satisfieth the longing soul, and filleth the hungry soul with goodness. Psalms 107:9

My TALK with God today ➤ **Day** **Date**

☐ Morning Prayer ☐ Evening Prayer

ASK IN FAITH

Three Things I am **THANKFUL** for Today:

What do I need forgiveness for?

1.

2.

3.

I turn this over to the Lord. **LET** go and let God handle it

Ask God to help with this challenge today.

Prayer with action makes a difference. I set these intentions for the day:

_____

_____

Ask the Lord to bless these people today.

_____

_____

_____

KEEP communicating with God today

For if ye forgive men their trespasses, your heavenly Father will also forgive you. But if ye forgive not men their trespasses, neither will your Father forgive your trespasses.
Matthew 6:14-15

Promptings from the Spirit   Blessings I received today

_____   _____

_____   _____

_____   _____

_____   _____

_____   _____

My TALK with God today | Day | **Date**

❏ Morning Prayer | ❏ Evening Prayer

ASK IN FAITH

Three Things I am **THANKFUL** for Today:

1.

2.

3.

I turn this over to the Lord. **LET** go and let God handle it

What do I need forgiveness for?

Ask God to help with this challenge today.

Prayer with action makes a difference. I set these intentions for the day:

_____

_____

_____

_____

_____

Ask the Lord to bless these people today.

KEEP communicating with God today

Promptings from the Spirit | Blessings I received today

_____ | _____

_____ | _____

_____ | _____

_____ | _____

For it is by faith that miracles are wrought; and it is by faith that angels appear and minister unto men.
Moroni 7:37

| My TALK with God today | Day | Date |

☐ **Morning Prayer** ☐ **Evening Prayer**

ASK IN FAITH

Three Things I am **THANKFUL** for Today:

1.

2.

3.

What do I need forgiveness for?

I turn this over to the Lord. **LET** go and let God handle it

Ask God to help with this challenge today.

Prayer with action makes a difference. I set these intentions for the day:

_____

_____

_____

_____

_____

Ask the Lord to bless these people today.

KEEP communicating with God today

Promptings from the Spirit   **Blessings I received today**

_____   _____

_____   _____

_____   _____

_____   _____

_____   _____

For those who, for whatever reason, fall into temptation and are dwelling upon unrighteous actions, I assure you that there is a way back, that there is hope in Christ.
Ulisses Soares

My TALK with God today ➤ **Day** **Date**

☐ **Morning Prayer** ☐ **Evening Prayer**

ASK IN FAITH

Three Things I am **THANKFUL** for Today:

1.

2.

3.

What do I need forgiveness for?

I turn this over to the Lord. **LET** go and let God handle it

Ask God to help with this challenge today.

Prayer with action makes a difference. I set these intentions for the day:

_____

_____

_____

_____

_____

Ask the Lord to bless these people today.

KEEP communicating with God today

Promptings from the Spirit   **Blessings I received today**

_____ _____

_____ _____

_____ _____

_____ _____

_____ _____

For thou art an holy people unto the Lord thy God: the Lord thy God hath chosen thee to be a special people unto himself, above all people that are upon the face of the earth. Deuteronomy 7:6

My TALK with God today | **Day** | **Date**

| ☐ Morning Prayer | ☐ Evening Prayer | **ASK IN FAITH** |

Three Things I am **THANKFUL** for Today:

What do I need forgiveness for?

1.

2.

3.

I turn this over to the Lord. **LET** go and let God handle it

Ask God to help with this challenge today.

Prayer with action makes a difference. I set these intentions for the day:

_____

_____

_____

_____

_____

Ask the Lord to bless these people today.

KEEP communicating with God today

Promptings from the Spirit   **Blessings I received today**

For we are made partakers of Christ, if we hold the beginning of our confidence steadfast unto the end.
Hebrews 3:14

My TALK with God today **Day**   **Date**

❑ Morning Prayer	❑ Evening Prayer	**ASK IN FAITH**

Three Things I am **THANKFUL** for Today:

1.

2.

3.

I turn this over to the Lord. **LET** go and let God handle it

What do I need forgiveness for?

Ask God to help with this challenge today.

Prayer with action makes a difference. I set these intentions for the day:

_____

_____

_____

_____

_____

Ask the Lord to bless these people today.

KEEP communicating with God today

Promptings from the Spirit	Blessings I received today
_____	_____
_____	_____
_____	_____
_____	_____
_____	_____

If we live in the Spirit, let us also walk in the Spirit. Galatians 5:25

My TALK with God today → **Day**　　　　　　**Date**

☐ Morning Prayer	☐ Evening Prayer

Three Things I am **THANKFUL** for Today:

1.

2.

3.

I turn this over to the Lord. **LET** go and let God handle it

Prayer with action makes a difference. I set these intentions for the day:

_____

_____

_____

_____

_____

ASK IN FAITH

What do I need forgiveness for?

Ask God to help with this challenge today.

Ask the Lord to bless these people today.

KEEP communicating with God today

Promptings from the Spirit	Blessings I received today
_____	_____
_____	_____
_____	_____
_____	_____
_____	_____

For we walk by faith, not by sight.
2 Corinthians 5:7

My TALK with God today ➤ **Day**   **Date**

☐ Morning Prayer	☐ Evening Prayer

ASK IN FAITH

Three Things I am **THANKFUL** for Today:
1.
2.
3.

What do I need forgiveness for?

I turn this over to the Lord. **LET** go and let God handle it

Ask God to help with this challenge today.

Prayer with action makes a difference. I set these intentions for the day:

_____

_____

_____

_____

_____

Ask the Lord to bless these people today.

KEEP communicating with God today

Promptings from the Spirit	Blessings I received today
_____	_____
_____	_____
_____	_____
_____	_____

For whosoever will save his life shall lose it: and whosoever will lose his life for my sake shall find it.
Matthew 16:25

My TALK with God today → **Day**   **Date**

❏ Morning Prayer	❏ Evening Prayer

ASK IN FAITH

Three Things I am **THANKFUL** for Today:
1.
2.
3.

What do I need forgiveness for?

I turn this over to the Lord. **LET** go and let God handle it

Ask God to help with this challenge today.

Prayer with action makes a difference. I set these intentions for the day:

_____

_____

_____

_____

_____

Ask the Lord to bless these people today.

KEEP communicating with God today

Promptings from the Spirit	Blessings I received today
_____	_____
_____	_____
_____	_____
_____	_____
_____	_____

For with God nothing shall be impossible.
Like 1:37

My TALK with God today ➤ **Day**　　　　　　**Date**

❏　Morning Prayer　　❏　Evening Prayer

ASK IN FAITH

What do I need forgiveness for?

Three Things I am **THANKFUL** for Today:
1.
2.
3.

I turn this over to the Lord. **LET** go and let God handle it

Ask God to help with this challenge today.

Prayer with action makes a difference. I set these intentions for the day:

_____

_____

_____

_____

_____

Ask the Lord to bless these people today.

KEEP communicating with God today

Promptings from the Spirit　　**Blessings I received today**

_____　　_____

_____　　_____

_____　　_____

_____　　_____

_____　　_____

For ye are all the children of God by faith in Christ Jesus. Galatians 3:26

My TALK with God today → **Day**   **Date**

□ **Morning Prayer**   □ **Evening Prayer** | **ASK IN FAITH**

What do I need forgiveness for?

Three Things I am **THANKFUL** for Today:

1.

2.

3.

I turn this over to the Lord. **LET** go and let God handle it

Ask God to help with this challenge today.

Prayer with action makes a difference. I set these intentions for the day:

_____

_____

_____

_____

_____

Ask the Lord to bless these people today.

KEEP communicating with God today

Promptings from the Spirit   **Blessings I received today**

_____   _____

_____   _____

_____   _____

_____   _____

_____   _____

Glory to God in the highest, and on earth peace, good will toward men.
Luke 2:14

My TALK with God today   **Day**   **Date**

☐ Morning Prayer	☐ Evening Prayer

ASK IN FAITH

Three Things I am **THANKFUL** for Today:
1.
2.
3.

I turn this over to the Lord. **LET** go and let God handle it

What do I need forgiveness for?

Ask God to help with this challenge today.

Prayer with action makes a difference. I set these intentions for the day:

_____

_____

_____

_____

_____

Ask the Lord to bless these people today.

KEEP communicating with God today

Promptings from the Spirit	Blessings I received today
_____	_____
_____	_____
_____	_____
_____	_____
_____	_____

Go forward in life with a twinkle in your eye and a smile on your face, but with great purpose in heart.
Gordon B. Hinckley

My TALK with God today ➤ Day   Date

☐ Morning Prayer   ☐ Evening Prayer

Three Things I am **THANKFUL** for Today:
1.
2.
3.

I turn this over to the Lord. **LET** go and let God handle it

Prayer with action makes a difference. I set these intentions for the day:

_____

_____

_____

_____

_____

KEEP communicating with God today

Promptings from the Spirit   Blessings I received today

_____   _____

_____   _____

_____   _____

_____   _____

_____   _____

ASK IN FAITH

What do I need forgiveness for?

Ask God to help with this challenge today.

Ask the Lord to bless these people today.

God does not begin by asking us about our ability, but only about our availability, and if we then prove our dependability, he will increase our capability.
Neal A. Maxwell

My TALK with God today → **Day** **Date**

☐ **Morning Prayer** ☐ **Evening Prayer**

Three Things I am **THANKFUL** for Today:	
1.	
2.	
3.	

I turn this over to the Lord. **LET** go and let God handle it

ASK IN FAITH

What do I need forgiveness for?

Ask God to help with this challenge today.

Prayer with action makes a difference. I set these intentions for the day:

_____
_____
_____
_____
_____

Ask the Lord to bless these people today.

KEEP communicating with God today

Promptings from the Spirit	**Blessings I received today**
_____	_____
_____	_____
_____	_____
_____	_____
_____	_____

God if mindful of every people, whatsoever land they be in.
Alma 26:37

My TALK with God today → **Day** **Date**

☐ Morning Prayer	☐ Evening Prayer

ASK IN FAITH

Three Things I am **THANKFUL** for Today:

1.

2.

3.

What do I need forgiveness for?

Turn this over to the Lord. **LET** go and let God handle it

Ask God to help with this challenge today.

Prayer with action makes a difference. I set these intentions for the day:

_____

_____

_____

_____

_____

Ask the Lord to bless these people today.

KEEP communicating with God today

Promptings from the Spirit   Blessings I received today

_____   _____

_____   _____

_____   _____

_____   _____

_____   _____

God is anxiously waiting for the chance to answer your prayers and fulfill your dreams, just as He always has. But He can't if you don't pray, and He can't if you don't dream. In short, He can't if you don't believe.
Jeffrey R Holland

My TALK with God today →　**Day**　　　　　　　**Date**

☐　**Morning Prayer**　　☐　**Evening Prayer**

ASK IN FAITH

Three Things I am **THANKFUL** for Today:
1.
2.
3.

What do I need forgiveness for?

Turn this over to the Lord. **LET** go and let God handle it

Ask God to help with this challenge today.

Prayer with action makes a difference. I set these intentions for the day:

_____

_____

_____

_____

_____

Ask the Lord to bless these people today.

KEEP communicating with God today

Promptings from the Spirit　　Blessings I received today

_____　_____

_____　_____

_____　_____

_____　_____

_____　_____

God not only loves the obedient - He enlightens them.
Henry B Eyring

My TALK with God today → **Day** **Date**

❑ Morning Prayer	❑ Evening Prayer	**ASK IN FAITH**

Three Things I am **THANKFUL** for Today:

What do I need forgiveness for?

1.

2.

3.

Turn this over to the Lord. **LET** go and let God handle it

Ask God to help with this challenge today.

Prayer with action makes a difference. I set these intentions for the day:

_____

_____

_____

Ask the Lord to bless these people today.

_____

_____

_____

KEEP communicating with God today

Promptings from the Spirit   Blessings I received today

_____   _____

_____   _____

_____   _____

_____   _____

_____   _____

God really is both just and merciful, giving to all who stand with Him "all that he hath." Jeffrey R. Holland

My TALK with God today	Day		Date

❏ Morning Prayer	❏ Evening Prayer

ASK IN FAITH

Three Things I am **THANKFUL** for Today:
1.
2.
3.

What do I need forgiveness for?

Turn this over to the Lord. **LET** go and let God handle it

Ask God to help with this challenge today.

Prayer with action makes a difference. I set these intentions for the day:

_____

_____

_____

_____

_____

Ask the Lord to bless these people today.

KEEP communicating with God today

Promptings from the Spirit	Blessings I received today
_____	_____
_____	_____
_____	_____
_____	_____
_____	_____

God will not desert us. He never has, and He never will. He cannot do it. It is not in His character to do so. George Q. Cannon

My TALK with God today → **Day** **Date**

☐ **Morning Prayer**	☐ **Evening Prayer**

ASK IN FAITH

Three Things I am **THANKFUL** for Today:

1.

2.

3.

Turn this over to the Lord. **LET** go and let God handle it

What do I need forgiveness for?

Ask God to help with this challenge today.

Prayer with action makes a difference. I set these intentions for the day:

_____

_____

_____

_____

_____

Ask the Lord to bless these people today.

KEEP communicating with God today

Promptings from the Spirit   Blessings I received today

_____   _____

_____   _____

_____   _____

_____   _____

_____   _____

Grace be to you, and peace, from God our Father, and from the Lord Jesus Christ. Ephesians 1:2

My TALK with God today **Day** **Date**

☐ **Morning Prayer**   ☐ **Evening Prayer**

ASK IN FAITH

Three Things I am **THANKFUL** for Today:

What do I need forgiveness for?

1.

2.

3.

Turn this over to the Lord. **LET** go and let God handle it

Ask God to help with this challenge today.

Prayer with action makes a difference. I set these intentions for the day:

_____

_____

_____

_____

_____

Ask the Lord to bless these people today.

KEEP communicating with God today

Promptings from the Spirit   **Blessings I received today**

_____   _____

_____   _____

_____   _____

_____   _____

_____   _____

Has anyone's burden been lighter today Because I was willing to share? Have the sick and the weary been helped on their way? When they needed my help was I there? Hymn 223

My TALK with God today → **Day** **Date**

☐ Morning Prayer ☐ Evening Prayer

ASK IN FAITH

Three Things I am **THANKFUL** for Today:

What do I need forgiveness for?

1.

2.

3.

Turn this over to the Lord. **LET** go and let God handle it

Ask God to help with this challenge today.

Prayer with action makes a difference. I set these intentions for the day:

_____

_____

Ask the Lord to bless these people today.

_____

_____

_____

KEEP communicating with God today

Promptings from the Spirit   Blessings I received today

_____   _____

_____   _____

_____   _____

_____   _____

_____   _____

Have I done any good in the world today? Have I helped anyone in need? Have I cheered up the sad and made someone feel glad? If not, I have failed indeed.
Hymn 223

My TALK with God today → **Day** **Date**

| ❑ Morning Prayer | ❑ Evening Prayer | **ASK IN FAITH** |

Three Things I am **THANKFUL** for Today:

1.

2.

3.

Turn this over to the Lord. **LET** go and let God handle it

What do I need forgiveness for?

Ask God to help with this challenge today.

Prayer with action makes a difference. I set these intentions for the day:

_____

_____

_____

_____

_____

Ask the Lord to bless these people today.

KEEP communicating with God today

Promptings from the Spirit   **Blessings I received today**

_____   _____

_____   _____

_____   _____

_____   _____

_____   _____

Having faith on the Lord;
having a hope that ye
shall receive eternal life;
having the love of God
always in your hearts,
that ye may be lifted up
at the last day and enter
into his rest.
Alma 13:29

My TALK with God today → **Day**   **Date**

☐ Morning Prayer	☐ Evening Prayer

ASK IN FAITH

Three Things I am **THANKFUL** for Today:

1.

2.

3.

What do I need forgiveness for?

Turn this over to the Lord. **LET** go and let God handle it

Ask God to help with this challenge today.

Prayer with action makes a difference. I set these intentions for the day:

_____

_____

_____

_____

_____

Ask the Lord to bless these people today.

KEEP communicating with God today

Promptings from the Spirit   **Blessings I received today**

_____   _____

_____   _____

_____   _____

_____   _____

_____   _____

He commandeth all men that they must repent, and be baptized in his name, having perfect faith in the Holy One of Israel, or they cannot be saved in the kingdom of God.
2 Nephi 9:23

My TALK with God today | **Day** | **Date**

☐ Morning Prayer ☐ Evening Prayer

ASK IN FAITH

Three Things I am **THANKFUL** for Today:

1.

2.

3.

I turn this over to the Lord. **LET** go and let God handle it

What do I need forgiveness for?

Ask God to help with this challenge today.

Prayer with action makes a difference. I set these intentions for the day:

_____

_____

_____

_____

_____

Ask the Lord to bless these people today..

KEEP communicating with God today

Promptings from the Spirit | Blessings I received today

_____ | _____

_____ | _____

_____ | _____

_____ | _____

_____ | _____

He giveth power to the faint; and to them that have no might he increaseth strength.
Isaiah 40:29

My TALK with God today → **Day**   **Date**

☐ Morning Prayer	☐ Evening Prayer	**ASK IN FAITH**

Three Things I am **THANKFUL** for Today:

What do I need forgiveness for?

1.

2.

3.

I turn this over to the Lord. **LET** go and let God handle it

Ask God to help with this challenge today.

Prayer with action makes a difference. I set these intentions for the day:

_____

Ask the Lord to bless these people today..

_____

_____

_____

_____

KEEP communicating with God today

Promptings from the Spirit	Blessings I received today

He revealeth the deep and secret things: he knoweth what is in the darkness, and the light dwelleth with him.
Daniel 2:22

My TALK with God today | **Day** | **Date**

☐ Morning Prayer	☐ Evening Prayer

ASK IN FAITH

Three Things I am **THANKFUL** for Today:

1.

2.

3.

I turn this over to the Lord. **LET** go and let God handle it

What do I need forgiveness for?

Ask God to help with this challenge today.

Prayer with action makes a difference. I set these intentions for the day:

_____

_____

_____

_____

_____

Ask the Lord to bless these people today..

KEEP communicating with God today

Promptings from the Spirit	Blessings I received today
_____	_____
_____	_____
_____	_____
_____	_____
_____	_____

He that believeth on me, as the scripture hath said, out of his belly shall flow rivers of living water.
John 7:38

My TALK with God today → **Day**   **Date**

☐ Morning Prayer	☐ Evening Prayer

ASK IN FAITH

Three Things I am **THANKFUL** for Today:

1.

2.

3.

What do I need forgiveness for?

I turn this over to the Lord. **LET** go and let God handle it

Ask God to help with this challenge today.

Prayer with action makes a difference. I set these intentions for the day:

_____

_____

_____

_____

_____

Ask the Lord to bless these people today..

KEEP communicating with God today

Promptings from the Spirit   **Blessings I received today**

_____   _____

_____   _____

_____   _____

_____   _____

_____   _____

Heal me, O Lord, and I shall be healed; save me, and I shall be saved: for thou art my praise.
Jeremiah 17:14

My TALK with God today → **Day**   **Date**

☐ **Morning Prayer**   ☐ **Evening Prayer**   **ASK IN FAITH**

Three Things I am **THANKFUL** for Today:

What do I need forgiveness for?

1.

2.

3.

I turn this over to the Lord. **LET** go and let God handle it

Ask God to help with this challenge today.

Prayer with action makes a difference. I set these intentions for the day:

_____

_____

_____   **Ask the Lord to bless these people today..**

_____

_____

KEEP communicating with God today

Promptings from the Spirit   **Blessings I received today**

_____   _____

_____   _____

_____   _____

_____   _____

_____   _____

Heavenly Father, now I pray, Guide and guard me every day. Help me feel thy love for me. This I humbly ask of thee. CSB Pg19

My TALK with God today   **Day**   **Date**

☐ Morning Prayer	☐ Evening Prayer

ASK IN FAITH

Three Things I am **THANKFUL** for Today:

1.

2.

3.

I turn this over to the Lord. **LET** go and let God handle it

What do I need forgiveness for?

Ask God to help with this challenge today.

Prayer with action makes a difference. I set these intentions for the day:

_____

_____

_____

_____

_____

Ask the Lord to bless these people today..

KEEP communicating with God today

Promptings from the Spirit   **Blessings I received today**

_____   _____

_____   _____

_____   _____

_____   _____

_____   _____

How we choose to deal with pain is ultimately the measure of who we are and of the success we have in closing our gaps.
Hyrum W Smith

My TALK with God today   → **Day**   **Date**

❑ Morning Prayer	❑ Evening Prayer

ASK IN FAITH

Three Things I am **THANKFUL** for Today:

1.

2.

3.

I turn this over to the Lord. **LET** go and let God handle it

What do I need forgiveness for?

Ask God to help with this challenge today.

Prayer with action makes a difference. I set these intentions for the day:

_____

_____

_____

_____

_____

Ask the Lord to bless these people today..

KEEP communicating with God today

Promptings from the Spirit	Blessings I received today
_____	_____
_____	_____
_____	_____
_____	_____
_____	_____

Heavenly Father, are you really there? And do you hear and answer every child's prayer? Some say that heaven is far away, but I feel it close around me as I pray.
CSB Pg12

My TALK with God today **Day** **Date**

☐ **Morning Prayer** ☐ **Evening Prayer**

| Three Things I am **THANKFUL** for Today: |
| 1. |
| 2. |
| 3. |

I turn this over to the Lord. **LET** go and let God handle it

Prayer with action makes a difference. I set these
intentions for the day:

_____

_____

_____

_____

_____

KEEP communicating with God today

Promptings from the Spirit   **Blessings I received today**

_____   _____

_____   _____

_____   _____

_____   _____

_____   _____

ASK IN FAITH

**What do I need
forgiveness for?**

**Ask God to help with this
challenge today.**

**Ask the Lord to bless
these people today..**

That which is of God
inviteth and enticeth to
do good continually;
wherefore, every thing
which inviteth and
enticeth to do good, and
to love God, and to
serve him, is
inspired of God.
Moroni 7:13

My TALK with God today | Day | Date

| ☐ Morning Prayer | ☐ Evening Prayer |

ASK IN FAITH

Three Things I am **THANKFUL** for Today:

1.

2.

3.

What do I need forgiveness for?

I turn this over to the Lord. **LET** go and let God handle it

Ask God to help with this challenge today.

Prayer with action makes a difference. I set these intentions for the day:

_____

_____

_____

_____

_____

Ask the Lord to bless these people today..

KEEP communicating with God today

Promptings from the Spirit | Blessings I received today

_____ | _____

_____ | _____

_____ | _____

_____ | _____

_____ | _____

That your faith should not stand in the wisdom of men, but in the power of God.
1 Corinthians 2:5

My TALK with God today   Day   Date

☐ Morning Prayer	☐ Evening Prayer

ASK IN FAITH

Three Things I am **THANKFUL** for Today:

1.

2.

3.

I turn this over to the Lord. **LET** go and let God handle it

What do I need forgiveness for?

Prayer with action makes a difference. I set these intentions for the day:

_____

_____

_____

_____

_____

Ask God to help with this challenge today.

Ask the Lord to bless these people today.

KEEP communicating with God today

Promptings from the Spirit   Blessings I received today

_____   _____

_____   _____

_____   _____

_____   _____

_____   _____

Help us now thy will to do. Make us loving, kind, and true. Through the day and through the night, lead us by thy holy light.
CSB Pg24

My TALK with God today ➤ **Day** **Date**

❑ **Morning Prayer** ❑ **Evening Prayer**

ASK IN FAITH

Three Things I am **THANKFUL** for Today:

1.

2.

3.

I turn this over to the Lord. **LET** go and let God handle it

What do I need forgiveness for?

Prayer with action makes a difference. I set these intentions for the day:

_____

_____

_____

_____

_____

Ask God to help with this challenge today.

Ask the Lord to bless these people today.

KEEP communicating with God today

Promptings from the Spirit   Blessings I received today

_____   _____

_____   _____

_____   _____

_____   _____

_____   _____

I say unto you that ye must pray always, and not faint.
2 Nephi 32:9

My TALK with God today   **Day**   **Date**

☐ Morning Prayer	☐ Evening Prayer	**ASK IN FAITH**

Three Things I am **THANKFUL** for Today:	**What do I need forgiveness for?**
1.	
2.	
3.	

I turn this over to the Lord. **LET** go and let God handle it

Ask God to help with this challenge today.

Prayer with action makes a difference. I set these intentions for the day:

_____

_____

Ask the Lord to bless these people today.

_____

_____

_____

KEEP communicating with God today

Promptings from the Spirit	Blessings I received today
_____	_____
_____	_____
_____	_____
_____	_____
_____	_____

His concern is for the faith at which you finally arrive, not the hour of the day in which you got there.
Jeffrey R. Holland

My TALK with God today → **Day**   **Date**

☐ Morning Prayer   ☐ Evening Prayer

ASK IN FAITH

Three Things I am **THANKFUL** for Today:

1.

2.

3.

What do I need forgiveness for?

I turn this over to the Lord. **LET** go and let God handle it

Ask God to help with this challenge today.

Prayer with action makes a difference. I set these intentions for the day:

_____

_____

_____

_____

_____

Ask the Lord to bless these people today.

KEEP communicating with God today

Promptings from the Spirit   Blessings I received today

_____   _____

_____   _____

_____   _____

_____   _____

_____   _____

His is a gospel of second and third chances, made possible by His atoning sacrifice. He invites each of us to be a good Samaritan, less judgmental and more forgiving of ourselves and of each other, even as we strive more fully to keep His commandments.
Gerrit W Gong

My TALK with God today   **Day**   **Date**

☐ Morning Prayer	☐ Evening Prayer

ASK IN FAITH

Three Things I am **THANKFUL** for Today:

What do I need
forgiveness for?

1.

2.

3.

I turn this over to the Lord. **LET** go and let God handle it

Ask God to help with this
challenge today.

**Prayer with action makes a difference. I set these
intentions for the day:**

_____

_____

Ask the Lord to bless
these people today.

_____

_____

_____

KEEP communicating with God today

Promptings from the Spirit   **Blessings I received today**

_____   _____

_____   _____

_____   _____

_____   _____

_____   _____

How could the Father
show the world the
pathway we should go?
He sent his Son to walk
with men on earth, that
we may know.
CBS Pg34

My TALK with God today | **Day** | **Date**

☐ Morning Prayer	☐ Evening Prayer

ASK IN FAITH

Three Things I am **THANKFUL** for Today:

1.

2.

3.

I turn this over to the Lord. **LET** go and let God handle it

What do I need forgiveness for?

Ask God to help with this challenge today.

Prayer with action makes a difference. I set these intentions for the day:

_____

_____

_____

_____

_____

Ask the Lord to bless these people today.

KEEP communicating with God today

Promptings from the Spirit

_____

_____

_____

_____

_____

Blessings I received today

_____

_____

_____

_____

_____

I will not leave you comfortless: I will come to you.
John 14:18

My TALK with God today ➤ Day   Date

☐ Morning Prayer	☐ Evening Prayer	**ASK IN FAITH**

Three Things I am **THANKFUL** for Today:	What do I need forgiveness for?
1.	
2.	
3.	

I turn this over to the Lord. **LET** go and let God handle it

Ask God to help with this challenge today.

Prayer with action makes a difference. I set these intentions for the day:

_____

_____

_____

_____

_____

Ask the Lord to bless these people today.

KEEP communicating with God today

Promptings from the Spirit	Blessings I received today
_____	_____
_____	_____
_____	_____
_____	_____
_____	_____

I, the Lord, am bound when ye do what I say; but when ye do not what I say, ye have no promise.
D&C 82:10

My TALK with God today

Day

Date

☐ **Morning Prayer**   ☐ **Evening Prayer**

ASK IN FAITH

Three Things I am **THANKFUL** for Today:

1.

2.

3.

What do I need forgiveness for?

I turn this over to the Lord. **LET** go and let God handle it

Ask God to help with this challenge today.

Prayer with action makes a difference. I set these intentions for the day:

_____

_____

_____

_____

_____

Ask the Lord to bless these people today.

KEEP communicating with God today

Promptings from the Spirit

_____

_____

_____

_____

_____

Blessings I received today

_____

_____

_____

_____

_____

How could the Father tell the world of love and tenderness? He sent his Son, a newborn babe, with peace and holiness.
CSB Pg34

My TALK with God today   **Day**   **Date**

☐   Morning Prayer   ☐   Evening Prayer   **ASK IN FAITH**

Three Things I am **THANKFUL** for Today:
1.
2.
3.

What do I need forgiveness for?

I turn this over to the Lord. **LET** go and let God handle it

Ask God to help with this challenge today.

Prayer with action makes a difference. I set these intentions for the day:

_____

_____

_____

_____

_____

Ask the Lord to bless these people today.

KEEP communicating with God today

Promptings from the Spirit   Blessings I received today

_____ _____

_____ _____

_____ _____

_____ _____

_____ _____

If any of you lack wisdom, let him ask of God, that giveth to all men liberally, and upbraideth not; and it shall be given him.
James 1:5

My TALK with God today → **Day**   **Date**

| ☐ Morning Prayer | ☐ Evening Prayer | **ASK IN FAITH** |

Three Things I am **THANKFUL** for Today:

What do I need forgiveness for?

1.

2.

3.

I turn this over to the Lord. **LET** go and let God handle it

Ask God to help with this challenge today.

Prayer with action makes a difference. I set these intentions for the day:

_____

_____

Ask the Lord to bless these people today.

_____

_____

_____

KEEP communicating with God today

Promptings from the Spirit   Blessings I received today

_____   _____

_____   _____

_____   _____

_____   _____

_____   _____

How could the Father tell the world of sacrifice, of death? He sent his Son to die for us and rise with living breath.
CSB Pg34

My TALK with God today → **Day**

Date

☐ Morning Prayer ☐ Evening Prayer

ASK IN FAITH

Three Things I am **THANKFUL** for Today:

1.

2.

3.

What do I need forgiveness for?

I turn this over to the Lord. **LET** go and let God handle it

Ask God to help with this challenge today.

Prayer with action makes a difference. I set these intentions for the day:

_____

_____

_____

_____

_____

Ask the Lord to bless these people today.

KEEP communicating with God today

Promptings from the Spirit   Blessings I received today
_____   _____
_____   _____
_____   _____
_____   _____
_____   _____

How gentle God's commands! How kind his precepts are! Come, cast your burdens on the Lord And trust his constant care.
Hymn 125

My TALK with God today → **Day** **Date**

☐ Morning Prayer	☐ Evening Prayer

ASK IN FAITH

Three Things I am **THANKFUL** for Today:
1.
2.
3.

What do I need forgiveness for?

I turn this over to the Lord. **LET** go and let God handle it

Ask God to help with this challenge today.

Prayer with action makes a difference. I set these intentions for the day:

_____

_____

_____

_____

_____

Ask the Lord to bless these people today.

KEEP communicating with God today

Promptings from the Spirit	Blessings I received today
_____	_____
_____	_____
_____	_____
_____	_____
_____	_____

However late you think you are, however many chances you think you have missed, however many mistakes you feel you have made or talents you think you don't have, or however far from home and family and God you feel you have traveled, I testify that you have not traveled beyond the reach of divine love. Jeffry R Holland

My TALK with God today → **Day** **Date**

| ☐ Morning Prayer | ☐ Evening Prayer | **ASK IN FAITH** |

| Three Things I am **THANKFUL** for Today: | What do I need forgiveness for? |

1.

2.

3.

I turn this over to the Lord. **LET** go and let God handle it

Ask God to help with this challenge today.

Prayer with action makes a difference. I set these intentions for the day:

_____

_____

Ask the Lord to bless these people today.

_____

_____

_____

KEEP communicating with God today

Promptings from the Spirit   Blessings I received today

_____   _____

_____   _____

_____   _____

_____   _____

_____   _____

How great, how glorious, how complete redemption's grand design. Where justice, love, and mercy meet in harmony divine!
Hymn 195

My TALK with God today → **Day**   **Date**

☐   **Morning Prayer**   ☐   **Evening Prayer**

ASK IN FAITH

Three Things I am **THANKFUL** for Today:

1.

2.

3.

What do I need forgiveness for?

I turn this over to the Lord. **LET** go and let God handle it

Ask God to help with this challenge today.

Prayer with action makes a difference. I set these intentions for the day:

_____

_____

_____

_____

_____

Ask the Lord to bless these people today.

KEEP communicating with God today

Promptings from the Spirit   **Blessings I received today**

_____   _____

_____   _____

_____   _____

_____   _____

_____   _____

Humble yourselves in the sight of the Lord, and he shall lift you up.
James 4:10

My TALK with God today → Day

Date

☐ Morning Prayer ☐ Evening Prayer

ASK IN FAITH

What do I need forgiveness for?

Three Things I am **THANKFUL** for Today:

1.

2.

3.

I turn this over to the Lord. **LET** go and let God handle it

Ask God to help with this challenge today.

Prayer with action makes a difference. I set these intentions for the day:

_____

_____

_____

_____

_____

Ask the Lord to bless these people today.

KEEP communicating with God today

Promptings from the Spirit   **Blessings I received today**

_____   _____

_____   _____

_____   _____

_____   _____

_____   _____

I can do all things through Christ which strengtheneth me.
Philippians 4:13

My TALK with God today → **Day**   **Date**

☐ Morning Prayer   ☐ Evening Prayer   **ASK IN FAITH**

Three Things I am **THANKFUL** for Today:
1.
2.
3.

I turn this over to the Lord. **LET** go and let God handle it

What do I need forgiveness for?

Ask God to help with this challenge today.

Prayer with action makes a difference. I set these intentions for the day:

_____

_____

_____

_____

_____

Ask the Lord to bless these people today.

KEEP communicating with God today

Promptings from the Spirit   Blessings I received today

_____   _____

_____   _____

_____   _____

_____   _____

_____   _____

I feel my Savior's love in all the world around me. His Spirit warms my soul through everything I see.
CSB Pg74

My TALK with God today → **Day** _____ **Date** _____

☐ Morning Prayer ☐ Evening Prayer

ASK IN FAITH

Three Things I am **THANKFUL** for Today:
1.
2.
3.

I turn this over to the Lord. **LET** go and let God handle it

What do I need forgiveness for?

Ask God to help with this challenge today.

Prayer with action makes a difference. I set these intentions for the day:

_____

_____

_____

_____

Ask the Lord to bless these people today.

KEEP communicating with God today

Promptings from the Spirit   Blessings I received today

_____   _____

_____   _____

_____   _____

_____   _____

I give unto men weakness that they may be humble; and my grace is sufficient for all men that humble themselves before me; for if they humble themselves before me, and have faith in me, then will I make weak things become strong unto them.
Ether 12:27

My TALK with God today → Day   Date

❏ Morning Prayer	❏ Evening Prayer

ASK IN FAITH

Three Things I am **THANKFUL** for Today:
1.
2.
3.

What do I need forgiveness for?

I turn this over to the Lord. **LET** go and let God handle it

Ask God to help with this challenge today.

Prayer with action makes a difference. I set these intentions for the day:

_____

_____

_____

_____

_____

Ask the Lord to bless these people today.

KEEP communicating with God today

Promptings from the Spirit	Blessings I received today
_____	_____
_____	_____
_____	_____
_____	_____
_____	_____

I kneel to pray every day. I speak to Heavenly Father. He hears and answers me when I pray in faith.
CSB Pg14

My TALK with God today   Day   Date

❑ Morning Prayer	❑ Evening Prayer

ASK IN FAITH

Three Things I am **THANKFUL** for Today:

What do I need forgiveness for?

1.

2.

3.

Turn this over to the Lord. **LET** go and let God handle it

Ask God to help with this challenge today.

Prayer with action makes a difference. I set these intentions for the day:

_____

_____

Ask the Lord to bless these people today.

_____

_____

_____

KEEP communicating with God today

Promptings from the Spirit   Blessings I received today

_____ _____

_____ _____

_____ _____

_____ _____

_____ _____

Now the God of hope fill you with all joy and peace in believing, that ye may abound in hope, through the power of the Holy Ghost.
Romans 15:13

My TALK with God today → **Day**　　　　　　　**Date**

☐ Morning Prayer	☐ Evening Prayer

ASK IN FAITH

Three Things I am **THANKFUL** for Today:

1.

2.

3.

Turn this over to the Lord. **LET** go and let God handle it

What do I need forgiveness for?

Ask God to help with this challenge today.

Prayer with action makes a difference. I set these intentions for the day:

_____

_____

_____

_____

_____

Ask the Lord to bless these people today.

KEEP communicating with God today

Promptings from the Spirit　　　Blessings I received today

_____　　_____

_____　　_____

_____　　_____

_____　　_____

_____　　_____

Now then we are ambassadors for Christ, as though God did beseech you by us: we pray you in Christ's stead, be ye reconciled to God. 2 Corinthians 5:20

My TALK with God today → **Day**   **Date**

☐ Morning Prayer	☐ Evening Prayer

ASK IN FAITH

Three Things I am **THANKFUL** for Today:

1.

2.

3.

Turn this over to the Lord. **LET** go and let God handle it

What do I need forgiveness for?

Ask God to help with this challenge today.

Prayer with action makes a difference. I set these intentions for the day:

_____
_____
_____
_____
_____

Ask the Lord to bless these people today.

KEEP communicating with God today

Promptings from the Spirit	Blessings I received today
_____	_____
_____	_____
_____	_____
_____	_____
_____	_____

I know my Father lives and loves me too. The Spirit whispers this to me and tells me it is true.
CSB Pg5

My TALK with God today → **Day** **Date**

❏ Morning Prayer	❏ Evening Prayer

ASK IN FAITH

Three Things I am **THANKFUL** for Today:

1.

2.

3.

What do I need forgiveness for?

Turn this over to the Lord. **LET** go and let God handle it

Ask God to help with this challenge today.

Prayer with action makes a difference. I set these intentions for the day:

_____

_____

_____

_____

_____

Ask the Lord to bless these people today.

KEEP communicating with God today

Promptings from the Spirit	Blessings I received today
_____	_____
_____	_____
_____	_____
_____	_____
_____	_____

I know your lives are busy. I know that you have much to do. But I make you a promise that if you will go to the house of the Lord, you will be blessed; life will be better for you. Gordon B. Hinckley

My TALK with God today   **Day**   **Date**

❑ Morning Prayer	❑ Evening Prayer

ASK IN FAITH

What do I need forgiveness for?

Three Things I am **THANKFUL** for Today:

1.

2.

3.

Turn this over to the Lord. **LET** go and let God handle it

Ask God to help with this challenge today.

Prayer with action makes a difference. I set these intentions for the day:

_____

_____

_____

_____

_____

Ask the Lord to bless these people today.

KEEP communicating with God today

Promptings from the Spirit	Blessings I received today
_____	_____
_____	_____
_____	_____
_____	_____
_____	_____

Savior, Redeemer of my soul, whose mighty hand hath made me whole. Whose wondrous power hath raised me up and filled with sweet my bitter cup! What tongue my gratitude can tell, O gracious God of Israel. Hymn 112

My TALK with God today **Day** **Date**

☐ **Morning Prayer**   ☐ **Evening Prayer**

ASK IN FAITH

Three Things I am **THANKFUL** for Today:

What do I need forgiveness for?

1.

2.

3.

Turn this over to the Lord. **LET** go and let God handle it

Ask God to help with this challenge today.

Prayer with action makes a difference. I set these intentions for the day:

_____

_____

_____

_____

_____

Ask the Lord to bless these people today.

KEEP communicating with God today

Promptings from the Spirit   **Blessings I received today**

_____   _____

_____   _____

_____   _____

_____   _____

_____   _____

Search these commandments, for they are true and faithful, and the prophecies and promises which are in them shall all be fulfilled.
D&C 1:37

My TALK with God today   **Day**   **Date**

❑ Morning Prayer	❑ Evening Prayer	**ASK IN FAITH**

Three Things I am **THANKFUL** for Today:

What do I need forgiveness for?

1.

2.

3.

Turn this over to the Lord. **LET** go and let God handle it

Ask God to help with this challenge today.

Prayer with action makes a difference. I set these intentions for the day:

_____

_____

_____

_____

_____

Ask the Lord to bless these people today.

KEEP communicating with God today

Promptings from the Spirit   **Blessings I received today**

_____ _____

_____ _____

_____ _____

_____ _____

_____ _____

I need my Heavenly Father to help me every day. He wants me to be happy and choose the righteous way.
CSB Pg18

My TALK with God today

Day

Date

☐ Morning Prayer ☐ Evening Prayer

ASK IN FAITH

What do I need forgiveness for?

Three Things I am **THANKFUL** for Today:

1.

2.

3.

Turn this over to the Lord. **LET** go and let God handle it

Ask God to help with this challenge today.

Prayer with action makes a difference. I set these intentions for the day:

_____

Ask the Lord to bless these people today.

_____

_____

_____

_____

KEEP communicating with God today

Promptings from the Spirit   Blessings I received today

_____ _____

_____ _____

_____ _____

_____ _____

_____ _____

I need thee every hour;
Stay thou nearby.
Temptations lose their
power when
thou art nigh.
Hymn 98

My TALK with God today ➤ Day _____   Date _____

☐ Morning Prayer	☐ Evening Prayer

Three Things I am **THANKFUL** for Today:

1.

2.

3.

Turn this over to the Lord. **LET** go and let God handle it

Prayer with action makes a difference. I set these intentions for the day:

_____

_____

_____

_____

KEEP communicating with God today

Promptings from the Spirit   **Blessings I received today**

_____   _____

_____   _____

_____   _____

_____   _____

_____   _____

ASK IN FAITH

What do I need forgiveness for?

Ask God to help with this challenge today.

Ask the Lord to bless these people today.

I promise that the spiritual gift of revelation will attend your call to the work of proclaiming the gospel and your assignment to a specific field or fields of labor.
David A Bednar

My TALK with God today	Day	Date

☐ Morning Prayer	☐ Evening Prayer

ASK IN FAITH

Three Things I am **THANKFUL** for Today:
1.
2.
3.

What do I need forgiveness for?

I turn this over to the Lord. **LET** go and let God handle it

Ask God to help with this challenge today.

Prayer with action makes a difference. I set these intentions for the day:

_____

_____

_____

_____

_____

Ask the Lord to bless these people today..

KEEP communicating with God today

Promptings from the Spirit	Blessings I received today
_____	_____
_____	_____
_____	_____
_____	_____
_____	_____

I testify of the joy to be found in living by faith, believing without seeing, but knowing by the power of the Holy Ghost that
Jesus Christ lives.
S Mark Palmer

My TALK with God today → **Day**   **Date**

☐ Morning Prayer	☐ Evening Prayer

ASK IN FAITH

Three Things I am **THANKFUL** for Today:

1.

2.

3.

I turn this over to the Lord. **LET** go and let God handle it

What do I need forgiveness for?

Prayer with action makes a difference. I set these intentions for the day:

_____

_____

_____

_____

_____

Ask God to help with this challenge today.

Ask the Lord to bless these people today..

KEEP communicating with God today

Promptings from the Spirit	Blessings I received today
_____	_____
_____	_____
_____	_____
_____	_____
_____	_____

I thank thee, dear Father in heaven above, for thy goodness and mercy, thy kindness and love.
CSB Pg7

My TALK with God today **Day** **Date**

❏ **Morning Prayer** ❏ **Evening Prayer**

ASK IN FAITH

Three Things I am **THANKFUL** for Today:

1.

2.

3.

I turn this over to the Lord. **LET** go and let God handle it

What do I need forgiveness for?

Ask God to help with this challenge today.

Prayer with action makes a difference. I set these intentions for the day:

_____

_____

_____

_____

_____

Ask the Lord to bless these people today..

KEEP communicating with God today

Promptings from the Spirit **Blessings I received today**

_____ _____

_____ _____

_____ _____

_____ _____

_____ _____

I will be on your right hand and on your left, and my Spirit shall be in your hearts, and mine angels around about you, to bear you up.
D&C 84:88

My TALK with God today

Day

Date

☐ Morning Prayer | ☐ Evening Prayer

ASK IN FAITH

Three Things I am **THANKFUL** for Today:

1.

2.

3.

I turn this over to the Lord. **LET** go and let God handle it

What do I need forgiveness for?

Ask God to help with this challenge today.

Prayer with action makes a difference. I set these intentions for the day:

_____

_____

_____

_____

_____

Ask the Lord to bless these people today..

KEEP communicating with God today

Promptings from the Spirit | **Blessings I received today**

_____ | _____

_____ | _____

_____ | _____

_____ | _____

_____ | _____

I will go and do the things which the Lord hath commanded, for I know that the Lord giveth no commandments unto the children of men, save he shall prepare a way for them that they may accomplish the thing which he commandeth them.
1 Nephi 3:7

My TALK with God today → **Day** | **Date**

☐ **Morning Prayer** | ☐ **Evening Prayer**

ASK IN FAITH

Three Things I am **THANKFUL** for Today:

1.

2.

3.

I turn this over to the Lord. **LET** go and let God handle it

What do I need forgiveness for?

Ask God to help with this challenge today.

Prayer with action makes a difference. I set these intentions for the day:

_____

_____

_____

_____

_____

Ask the Lord to bless these people today..

KEEP communicating with God today

Promptings from the Spirit | Blessings I received today

_____ _____

_____ _____

_____ _____

_____ _____

_____ _____

I will impart unto you of my Spirit, which shall enlighten your mind, which shall fill your soul with joy.
D&C 11:13

My TALK with God today **Day** **Date**

☐ Morning Prayer	☐ Evening Prayer

ASK IN FAITH

Three Things I am **THANKFUL** for Today:

1.

2.

3.

What do I need forgiveness for?

I turn this over to the Lord. **LET** go and let God handle it

Ask God to help with this challenge today.

Prayer with action makes a difference. I set these intentions for the day:

_____

_____

_____

_____

_____

Ask the Lord to bless these people today..

KEEP communicating with God today

Promptings from the Spirit

Blessings I received today

_____ _____

_____ _____

_____ _____

_____ _____

_____ _____

I will not doubt, I will not fear; God's love and strength are always near. His promised gift helps me to find An inner strength and peace of mind. I give the Father willingly my trust, my prayers, humility. His Spirit guides; his love assures that fear departs when faith endures. Hymn 128

My TALK with God today	Day		Date

☐ Morning Prayer	☐ Evening Prayer

ASK IN FAITH

Three Things I am **THANKFUL** for Today:

1.

2.

3.

What do I need forgiveness for?

I turn this over to the Lord. **LET** go and let God handle it

Ask God to help with this challenge today.

Prayer with action makes a difference. I set these intentions for the day:

_____

_____

_____

_____

_____

Ask the Lord to bless these people today..

KEEP communicating with God today

Promptings from the Spirit	Blessings I received today
_____	_____
_____	_____
_____	_____
_____	_____
_____	_____

My son, peace be unto thy soul; thine adversity and thine afflictions shall be but a small moment. D&C 121:7

My TALK with God today

Day

Date

☐ **Morning Prayer**	☐ **Evening Prayer**

ASK IN FAITH

Three Things I am **THANKFUL** for Today:

1.

2.

3.

What do I need forgiveness for?

I turn this over to the Lord. **LET** go and let God handle it

Ask God to help with this challenge today.

Prayer with action makes a difference. I set these intentions for the day:

_____

_____

_____

_____

_____

Ask the Lord to bless these people today..

KEEP communicating with God today

Promptings from the Spirit	**Blessings I received today**
_____	_____
_____	_____
_____	_____
_____	_____
_____	_____

Never forget that you are a child of God, our Eternal Father, now and forever. He loves you.
M Russell Ballard

My TALK with God today	Day	Date

☐ Morning Prayer	☐ Evening Prayer

ASK IN FAITH

Three Things I am **THANKFUL** for Today:

1.

2.

3.

What do I need forgiveness for?

I turn this over to the Lord. **LET** go and let God handle it

Ask God to help with this challenge today.

Prayer with action makes a difference. I set these intentions for the day:

_____

_____

_____

_____

_____

Ask the Lord to bless these people today..

KEEP communicating with God today

Promptings from the Spirit	Blessings I received today
_____	_____
_____	_____
_____	_____
_____	_____
_____	_____

If a man be meek and lowly in heart, and confesses by the power of the Holy Ghost that Jesus is the Christ, he must needs have charity; for if he have not charity he is nothing.
Moroni 7:44

My TALK with God today　　Day　　　　　　　Date

☐ Morning Prayer	☐ Evening Prayer

ASK IN FAITH

Three Things I am **THANKFUL** for Today:

1.

2.

3.

I turn this over to the Lord. **LET** go and let God handle it

What do I need forgiveness for?

Ask God to help with this challenge today.

Prayer with action makes a difference. I set these intentions for the day:

_____

_____

_____

_____

_____

Ask the Lord to bless these people today.

KEEP communicating with God today

Promptings from the Spirit	Blessings I received today
_____	_____
_____	_____
_____	_____
_____	_____
_____	_____

If any man serve me, let him follow me; and where I am, there shall also my servant be: if any man serve me, him will my Father honor.
John 12:26

My TALK with God today   **Day**   **Date**

❑ Morning Prayer	❑ Evening Prayer

ASK IN FAITH

Three Things I am **THANKFUL** for Today:
1.
2.
3.

What do I need forgiveness for?

I turn this over to the Lord. **LET** go and let God handle it

Ask God to help with this challenge today.

Prayer with action makes a difference. I set these intentions for the day:

_____

_____

_____

_____

_____

Ask the Lord to bless these people today.

KEEP communicating with God today

Promptings from the Spirit   **Blessings I received today**

_____ _____

_____ _____

_____ _____

_____ _____

_____ _____

If with all your hearts ye truly seek me, ye shall ever surely find me. Thus saith our God.
CSB Pg15

My TALK with God today ➤ **Day**   **Date**

❏ Morning Prayer	❏ Evening Prayer

ASK IN FAITH

What do I need forgiveness for?

Three Things I am **THANKFUL** for Today:

1.

2.

3.

I turn this over to the Lord. **LET** go and let God handle it

Ask God to help with this challenge today.

Prayer with action makes a difference. I set these intentions for the day:

_____

_____

_____

Ask the Lord to bless these people today.

_____

_____

KEEP communicating with God today

Promptings from the Spirit   **Blessings I received today**

_____ _____

_____ _____

_____ _____

_____ _____

_____ _____

If ye have faith as a grain of mustard seed, ye shall say unto this mountain, remove hence to yonder place; and it shall remove; and nothing shall be impossible unto you.
Matthew 17:20

| My TALK with God today | Day | Date |

☐ **Morning Prayer**   ☐ **Evening Prayer**

ASK IN FAITH

Three Things I am **THANKFUL** for Today:

1.

2.

3.

I turn this over to the Lord. **LET** go and let God handle it

What do I need forgiveness for?

Ask God to help with this challenge today.

Prayer with action makes a difference. I set these intentions for the day:

_____

_____

_____

_____

_____

Ask the Lord to bless these people today.

KEEP communicating with God today

Promptings from the Spirit   Blessings I received today

_____   _____

_____   _____

_____   _____

_____   _____

_____   _____

If ye love me, keep my commandments.
John 14:15

My TALK with God today **Day** **Date**

☐ Morning Prayer	☐ Evening Prayer

ASK IN FAITH

Three Things I am **THANKFUL** for Today:

What do I need forgiveness for?

1.

2.

3.

I turn this over to the Lord. **LET** go and let God handle it

Ask God to help with this challenge today.

Prayer with action makes a difference. I set these intentions for the day:

_____

_____

Ask the Lord to bless these people today.

_____

_____

_____

KEEP communicating with God today

Promptings from the Spirit	Blessings I received today
_____	_____
_____	_____
_____	_____
_____	_____
_____	_____

If you are there for the Lord, He will be there for you. If you love Him and keep His commandments, you will have His Spirit to be with you and guide you.
Robert D Hales

My TALK with God today **Day** **Date**

☐ Morning Prayer	☐ Evening Prayer

ASK IN FAITH

Three Things I am **THANKFUL** for Today:

1.

2.

3.

What do I need forgiveness for?

I turn this over to the Lord. **LET** go and let God handle it

Ask God to help with this challenge today.

Prayer with action makes a difference. I set these intentions for the day:

_____
_____
_____
_____
_____

Ask the Lord to bless these people today.

KEEP communicating with God today

Promptings from the Spirit	Blessings I received today
_____	_____
_____	_____
_____	_____
_____	_____

If you're serious about sanctification, you can expect to experience heart-wrenching moments that try your faith, your endurance, and your patience.
Sheri Dew

My TALK with God today	Day	Date

☐ Morning Prayer	☐ Evening Prayer	ASK IN FAITH

Three Things I am **THANKFUL** for Today:

1.

2.

3.

I turn this over to the Lord. **LET** go and let God handle it

Prayer with action makes a difference. I set these intentions for the day:

_____

_____

_____

_____

_____

What do I need forgiveness for?

Ask God to help with this challenge today.

Ask the Lord to bless these people today.

KEEP communicating with God today

Promptings from the Spirit	Blessings I received today
_____	_____
_____	_____
_____	_____
_____	_____
_____	_____

If your self-worth is dependent on anything external, you are in big trouble.
Hyrum W Smith

My TALK with God today	Day	Date

☐ Morning Prayer	☐ Evening Prayer

ASK IN FAITH

Three Things I am THANKFUL for Today:

1.

2.

3.

I turn this over to the Lord. **LET** go and let God handle it

What do I need forgiveness for?

Ask God to help with this challenge today.

Prayer with action makes a difference. I set these intentions for the day:

_____

_____

_____

_____

_____

Ask the Lord to bless these people today.

KEEP communicating with God today

Promptings from the Spirit	Blessings I received today
_____	_____
_____	_____
_____	_____
_____	_____
_____	_____

In the day of prosperity be joyful, but in the day of adversity consider: God also hath set the one over against the other, to the end that man should find nothing after him.
Ecclesiastes 7:14

My TALK with God today ➤ **Day**   **Date**

☐ Morning Prayer	☐ Evening Prayer

ASK IN FAITH

Three Things I am **THANKFUL** for Today:

1.

2.

3.

I turn this over to the Lord. **LET** go and let God handle it

What do I need forgiveness for?

Ask God to help with this challenge today.

Prayer with action makes a difference. I set these intentions for the day:

_____

_____

_____

_____

_____

Ask the Lord to bless these people today.

KEEP communicating with God today

Promptings from the Spirit	Blessings I received today
_____	_____
_____	_____
_____	_____
_____	_____
_____	_____

Inch by inch, life's a cinch. Yard by yard, life's hard.
John Bytheway

My TALK with God today   **Day**

Date

☐ Morning Prayer	☐ Evening Prayer

ASK IN FAITH

Three Things I am **THANKFUL** for Today:
1.
2.
3.

I turn this over to the Lord. **LET** go and let God handle it

What do I need forgiveness for?

Ask God to help with this challenge today.

Prayer with action makes a difference. I set these intentions for the day:

_____

_____

_____

_____

_____

Ask the Lord to bless these people today.

KEEP communicating with God today

Promptings from the Spirit	Blessings I received today
_____	_____
_____	_____
_____	_____
_____	_____
_____	_____

The Lord bless thee, and keep thee: The Lord make his face ashine upon thee, and be gracious unto thee: The Lord lift up his countenance upon thee, and give thee peace.
Numbers 6:24-26

My TALK with God today ➡ **Day** **Date**

| ☐ **Morning Prayer** | ☐ **Evening Prayer** |

| Three Things I am **THANKFUL** for Today: |
| 1. |
| 2. |
| 3. |

I turn this over to the Lord. **LET** go and let God handle it

ASK IN FAITH

What do I need forgiveness for?

Ask God to help with this challenge today.

Prayer with action makes a difference. I set these intentions for the day:

_____

_____

_____

_____

_____

Ask the Lord to bless these people today.

KEEP communicating with God today

Promptings from the Spirit	**Blessings I received today**
_____	_____
_____	_____
_____	_____
_____	_____
_____	_____

Indeed, nothing is more critically connected to happiness—both our own and that of our children—than how well we love and support one another within the family.
M. Russell Ballard

My TALK with God today → **Day**   **Date**

☐ Morning Prayer	☐ Evening Prayer

ASK IN FAITH

Three Things I am **THANKFUL** for Today:
1.
2.
3.

What do I need
forgiveness for?

I turn this over to the Lord. **LET** go and let God handle it

Ask God to help with this
challenge today.

**Prayer with action makes a difference. I set these
intentions for the day:**

_____

_____

_____

_____

_____

Ask the Lord to bless
these people today.

KEEP communicating with God today

Promptings from the Spirit   **Blessings I received today**

_____   _____

_____   _____

_____   _____

_____   _____

_____   _____

It is better to trust in
the Lord than to put
confidence in man.
Psalms 118:8

My TALK with God today → **Day**   **Date**

☐ **Morning Prayer**   ☐ **Evening Prayer**   **ASK IN FAITH**

Three Things I am **THANKFUL** for Today:
1.
2.
3.

I turn this over to the Lord. **LET** go and let God handle it

What do I need forgiveness for?

Ask God to help with this challenge today.

Prayer with action makes a difference. I set these intentions for the day:

_____

_____

_____

_____

_____

Ask the Lord to bless these people today.

KEEP communicating with God today

Promptings from the Spirit   **Blessings I received today**

_____   _____

_____   _____

_____   _____

_____   _____

_____   _____

It is not for you to know the times or the seasons, which the Father hath put in his own power.
Acts 1:7

My TALK with God today → **Day**   **Date**

☐ Morning Prayer	☐ Evening Prayer

ASK IN FAITH

Three Things I am **THANKFUL** for Today:
1.
2.
3.

What do I need forgiveness for?

I turn this over to the Lord. **LET** go and let God handle it

Ask God to help with this challenge today.

Prayer with action makes a difference. I set these intentions for the day:

_____

_____

_____

_____

_____

Ask the Lord to bless these people today.

KEEP communicating with God today

Promptings from the Spirit	Blessings I received today
_____	_____
_____	_____
_____	_____
_____	_____
_____	_____

It is not possible for you to sink lower than the infinite light of Christ's Atonement shines.
Jeffrey R. Holland

My TALK with God today → **Day**   **Date**

❑ Morning Prayer	❑ Evening Prayer

Three Things I am **THANKFUL** for Today:
1.
2.
3.

What do I need forgiveness for?

I turn this over to the Lord. **LET** go and let God handle it

Ask God to help with this challenge today.

Prayer with action makes a difference. I set these intentions for the day:

_____

_____

_____

_____

_____

Ask the Lord to bless these people today.

KEEP communicating with God today

Promptings from the Spirit	Blessings I received today
_____	_____
_____	_____
_____	_____
_____	_____
_____	_____

Jesus Christ sees people deeply. He sees individuals, their needs, and who they can become.
Michelle Craig

My TALK with God today   **Day**   **Date**

☐ **Morning Prayer**   ☐ **Evening Prayer**   ## ASK IN FAITH

Three Things I am **THANKFUL** for Today:
1.
2.
3.

I turn this over to the Lord. **LET** go and let God handle it

What do I need forgiveness for?

Ask God to help with this challenge today.

Prayer with action makes a difference. I set these intentions for the day:

_____

_____

_____

_____

Ask the Lord to bless these people today.

KEEP communicating with God today

Promptings from the Spirit   **Blessings I received today**

_____   _____

_____   _____

_____   _____

_____   _____

_____   _____

Jesus Christ the same yesterday, and today, and forever.
Hebrews 13:8

My TALK with God today → **Day**

Date

☐ Morning Prayer ☐ Evening Prayer

ASK IN FAITH

What do I need forgiveness for?

Three Things I am **THANKFUL** for Today:

1.

2.

3.

I turn this over to the Lord. **LET** go and let God handle it

Ask God to help with this challenge today.

Prayer with action makes a difference. I set these intentions for the day:

_____

_____

_____

_____

_____

Ask the Lord to bless these people today.

KEEP communicating with God today

Promptings from the Spirit   **Blessings I received today**

_____   _____

_____   _____

_____   _____

_____   _____

_____   _____

Jesus, Savior, pilot me over life's tempestuous sea; Unknown waves before me roll, hiding rock and treacherous shoal. Chart and compass came from thee; Jesus, Savior, pilot me.
Hymn 14

My TALK with God today **Day** **Date**

☐ Morning Prayer	☐ Evening Prayer

ASK IN FAITH

Three Things I am **THANKFUL** for Today:
1.
2.
3.

What do I need forgiveness for?

I turn this over to the Lord. **LET** go and let God handle it

Ask God to help with this challenge today.

Prayer with action makes a difference. I set these intentions for the day:

_____

_____

_____

_____

_____

Ask the Lord to bless these people today.

KEEP communicating with God today

Promptings from the Spirit   **Blessings I received today**

_____   _____

_____   _____

_____   _____

_____   _____

_____   _____

Know therefore that the Lord thy God, he is God, the faithful God, which keepeth covenant and mercy with them that love him and keep his commandments to a thousand generations. Deuteronomy 7:9

My TALK with God today → **Day** **Date**

☐ Morning Prayer	☐ Evening Prayer

ASK IN FAITH

Three Things I am **THANKFUL** for Today:
1.
2.
3.

What do I need forgiveness for?

Turn this over to the Lord. **LET** go and let God handle it

Ask God to help with this challenge today.

Prayer with action makes a difference. I set these intentions for the day:

_____

_____

_____

_____

_____

Ask the Lord to bless these people today.

KEEP communicating with God today

Promptings from the Spirit	Blessings I received today
_____	_____
_____	_____
_____	_____
_____	_____
_____	_____

Learning by faith requires spiritual, mental, and physical exertion and not just passive reception.
David A. Bednar

My TALK with God today → **Day**   **Date**

☐ **Morning Prayer**   ☐ **Evening Prayer**

ASK IN FAITH

Three Things I am **THANKFUL** for Today:

What do I need forgiveness for?

1.

2.

3.

Turn this over to the Lord. **LET** go and let God handle it

Ask God to help with this challenge today.

Prayer with action makes a difference. I set these intentions for the day:

_____

_____

_____

_____

_____

Ask the Lord to bless these people today.

KEEP communicating with God today

Promptings from the Spirit   **Blessings I received today**

_____   _____

_____   _____

_____   _____

_____   _____

_____   _____

Let all your things be done with charity.
1 Corinthians 16:14

My TALK with God today → **Day** | **Date**

☐ Morning Prayer | ☐ Evening Prayer

ASK IN FAITH

Three Things I am **THANKFUL** for Today:

1.

2.

3.

What do I need forgiveness for?

Turn this over to the Lord. **LET** go and let God handle it

Ask God to help with this challenge today.

Prayer with action makes a difference. I set these intentions for the day:

_____

_____

_____

_____

_____

Ask the Lord to bless these people today.

KEEP communicating with God today

Promptings from the Spirit | Blessings I received today

_____ | _____

_____ | _____

_____ | _____

_____ | _____

_____ | _____

Let brotherly love continue.
Hebrews 13:1

My TALK with God today	**Day**	**Date**

☐ Morning Prayer	☐ Evening Prayer	**ASK IN FAITH**

Three Things I am **THANKFUL** for Today:	**What do I need forgiveness for?**
1.	
2.	
3.	

Turn this over to the Lord. **LET** go and let God handle it

Ask God to help with this challenge today.

Prayer with action makes a difference. I set these intentions for the day:

_____

_____

_____

_____

_____

Ask the Lord to bless these people today.

KEEP communicating with God today	
Promptings from the Spirit	Blessings I received today

Let not your heart be troubled: ye believe in God, believe also in me.
John 14:1

My TALK with God today →　**Day**　　　　**Date**

☐　Morning Prayer	☐　Evening Prayer

ASK IN FAITH

What do I need forgiveness for?

Three Things I am **THANKFUL** for Today:

1.

2.

3.

Turn this over to the Lord. **LET** go and let God handle it

Ask God to help with this challenge today.

Prayer with action makes a difference. I set these intentions for the day:

_____

_____

_____

_____

_____

Ask the Lord to bless these people today.

KEEP communicating with God today

Promptings from the Spirit	**Blessings I received today**
_____	_____
_____	_____
_____	_____
_____	_____
_____	_____

Let the word of Christ dwell in you richly in all wisdom; teaching and admonishing one another in psalms and hymns and spiritual songs, singing with grace in your hearts to the Lord.
Colossians 3:16

My TALK with God today → **Day**   **Date**

☐ **Morning Prayer**   ☐ **Evening Prayer**

Three Things I am **THANKFUL** for Today:
1.
2.
3.

Turn this over to the Lord. **LET** go and let God handle it

Prayer with action makes a difference. I set these intentions for the day:

_____

_____

_____

_____

KEEP communicating with God today

Promptings from the Spirit

Blessings I received today

_____ _____

_____ _____

_____ _____

_____ _____

_____ _____

ASK IN FAITH

What do I need forgiveness for?

Ask God to help with this challenge today.

Ask the Lord to bless these people today.

Let thy bowels also be full of charity towards all men, and to the household of faith, and let virtue garnish thy thoughts unceasingly; then shall thy confidence wax strong in the presence of God. D&C 121:45

My TALK with God today → **Day** **Date**

☐ Morning Prayer	☐ Evening Prayer

ASK IN FAITH

Three Things I am **THANKFUL** for Today:

1.

2.

3.

Turn this over to the Lord. **LET** go and let God handle it

What do I need forgiveness for?

Ask God to help with this challenge today.

Prayer with action makes a difference. I set these intentions for the day:

_____

_____

_____

_____

_____

Ask the Lord to bless these people today.

KEEP communicating with God today

Promptings from the Spirit | Blessings I received today
_____ | _____
_____ | _____
_____ | _____
_____ | _____
_____ | _____

None of us come to this earth to gain our worth; we brought it with us.
Sheri Dew

My TALK with God today → **Day**   **Date**

☐ Morning Prayer	☐ Evening Prayer

ASK IN FAITH

Three Things I am **THANKFUL** for Today:

1.

2.

3.

Turn this over to the Lord. **LET** go and let God handle it

What do I need forgiveness for?

Ask God to help with this challenge today.

Prayer with action makes a difference. I set these intentions for the day:

_____

_____

_____

_____

_____

Ask the Lord to bless these people today.

KEEP communicating with God today

Promptings from the Spirit	Blessings I received today
_____	_____
_____	_____
_____	_____
_____	_____
_____	_____

Not every one that saith unto me, Lord, Lord, shall enter into the kingdom of heaven; but he that doeth the will of my Father who is in heaven.
3 Nephi 14:21

My TALK with God today   **Day**   **Date**

☐ **Morning Prayer**	☐ **Evening Prayer**

ASK IN FAITH

Three Things I am **THANKFUL** for Today:
1.
2.
3.

Turn this over to the Lord. **LET** go and let God handle it

What do I need forgiveness for?

Ask God to help with this challenge today.

Prayer with action makes a difference. I set these intentions for the day:

_____

_____

_____

_____

_____

Ask the Lord to bless these people today.

KEEP communicating with God today

Promptings from the Spirit	Blessings I received today
_____	_____
_____	_____
_____	_____
_____	_____
_____	_____

Let us cheerfully do all things that lie in our power; and then may we stand still, with the utmost assurance, to see the salvation of God, and for his arm to be revealed.
D&C 123:17

My TALK with God today → **Day** | **Date**

☐ **Morning Prayer** ☐ **Evening Prayer**

Three Things I am **THANKFUL** for Today:
1.
2.
3.

I turn this over to the Lord. **LET** go and let God handle it

Prayer with action makes a difference. I set these intentions for the day:

_____

_____

_____

_____

_____

KEEP communicating with God today

Promptings from the Spirit   **Blessings I received today**

_____   _____

_____   _____

_____   _____

_____   _____

_____   _____

ASK IN FAITH

What do I need forgiveness for?

Ask God to help with this challenge today.

Ask the Lord to bless these people today..

Let us never forget to pray. God lives. He is near. He is real. He is not only aware of us but cares for us. He is our Father. He is accessible to all who will seek Him. Gordon B. Hinckley

My TALK with God today	Day	Date

☐ Morning Prayer	☐ Evening Prayer

Three Things I am **THANKFUL** for Today:

1.

2.

3.

I turn this over to the Lord. **LET** go and let God handle it

Prayer with action makes a difference. I set these intentions for the day:

_____

_____

_____

_____

_____

KEEP communicating with God today

Promptings from the Spirit	Blessings I received today
_____	_____
_____	_____
_____	_____
_____	_____
_____	_____

ASK IN FAITH

What do I need forgiveness for?

Ask God to help with this challenge today.

Ask the Lord to bless these people today..

Let us search and try our ways, and turn again to the Lord. Lamentations 3:40

| My TALK with God today ➤ | Day | Date |

| ☐ Morning Prayer | ☐ Evening Prayer |

ASK IN FAITH

Three Things I am **THANKFUL** for Today:

1.

2.

3.

I turn this over to the Lord. **LET** go and let God handle it

Prayer with action makes a difference. I set these intentions for the day:

_____

_____

_____

_____

_____

What do I need forgiveness for?

Ask God to help with this challenge today.

Ask the Lord to bless these people today..

KEEP communicating with God today

| Promptings from the Spirit | Blessings I received today |

_____   _____

_____   _____

_____   _____

_____   _____

_____   _____

Let us therefore come boldly unto the throne of grace, that we may obtain mercy, and find grace to help in time of need.
Hebrews 4:16

My TALK with God today → **Day**   **Date**

<table>
<tr><td>☐ Morning Prayer</td><td>☐ Evening Prayer</td><td>ASK IN FAITH</td></tr>
</table>

Three Things I am **THANKFUL** for Today:	What do I need forgiveness for?
1.	
2.	
3.	

I turn this over to the Lord. **LET** go and let God handle it

Ask God to help with this challenge today.

Prayer with action makes a difference. I set these intentions for the day:

_____

_____

_____   Ask the Lord to bless these people today..

_____

_____

KEEP communicating with God today

Promptings from the Spirit	Blessings I received today
_____	_____
_____	_____
_____	_____
_____	_____
_____	_____

Let your light so shine before men, that they may see your good works, and glorify your Father which is in heaven.
Matthew 5:16

My TALK with God today **Day** **Date**

❏ **Morning Prayer**   ❏ **Evening Prayer**

Three Things I am **THANKFUL** for Today:
1.
2.
3.

I turn this over to the Lord. **LET** go and let God handle it

Prayer with action makes a difference. I set these intentions for the day:

_____

_____

_____

_____

_____

ASK IN FAITH

What do I need forgiveness for?

Ask God to help with this challenge today.

Ask the Lord to bless these people today..

KEEP communicating with God today

Promptings from the Spirit   **Blessings I received today**

_____   _____

_____   _____

_____   _____

_____   _____

_____   _____

Life without God is a life filled with fear. Life with God is a life filled with peace.
Russell M. Nelson

My TALK with God today

Day

Date

☐   **Morning Prayer**   ☐   **Evening Prayer**

Three Things I am **THANKFUL** for Today:

1.

2.

3.

I turn this over to the Lord. **LET** go and let God handle it

Prayer with action makes a difference. I set these intentions for the day:

_____

_____

_____

_____

_____

KEEP communicating with God today

Promptings from the Spirit   **Blessings I received today**

_____   _____

_____   _____

_____   _____

_____   _____

_____   _____

ASK IN FAITH

What do I need forgiveness for?

Ask God to help with this challenge today.

Ask the Lord to bless these people today..

Lift up your head and be of good cheer.
3 Nephi 1:13

My TALK with God today	Day	Date

☐ Morning Prayer	☐ Evening Prayer	ASK IN FAITH

Three Things I am **THANKFUL** for Today:

1.

2.

3.

What do I need forgiveness for?

I turn this over to the Lord. **LET** go and let God handle it

Ask God to help with this challenge today.

Prayer with action makes a difference. I set these intentions for the day:

_____

_____

_____

_____

_____

Ask the Lord to bless these people today..

KEEP communicating with God today

Promptings from the Spirit

Blessings I received today

_____ _____

_____ _____

_____ _____

_____ _____

_____ _____

Look unto me in every thought; doubt not, fear not. D&C 6:36

My TALK with God today → **Day** **Date**

☐ **Morning Prayer**	☐ **Evening Prayer**

ASK IN FAITH

What do I need forgiveness for?

Three Things I am **THANKFUL** for Today:

1.

2.

3.

I turn this over to the Lord. **LET** go and let God handle it

Ask God to help with this challenge today.

Prayer with action makes a difference. I set these intentions for the day:

_____

_____

_____

_____

_____

Ask the Lord to bless these people today..

KEEP communicating with God today

Promptings from the Spirit	**Blessings I received today**
_____	_____
_____	_____
_____	_____
_____	_____
_____	_____

Lord, how oft shall my brother sin against me, and I forgive him? till seven times? Jesus saith unto him, I say not unto thee, Until seven times: but, Until seventy times seven.
Matthew 18:21-22

My TALK with God today | Day | Date

| ☐ Morning Prayer | ☐ Evening Prayer |

| Three Things I am **THANKFUL** for Today: |

1.

2.

3.

I turn this over to the Lord. **LET** go and let God handle it

Prayer with action makes a difference. I set these intentions for the day:

_____

_____

_____

_____

_____

ASK IN FAITH

What do I need forgiveness for?

Ask God to help with this challenge today.

Ask the Lord to bless these people today..

KEEP communicating with God today

Promptings from the Spirit

_____

_____

_____

_____

_____

Blessings I received today

_____

_____

_____

_____

_____

Love is the only force that can erase the differences between people or bridge the chasms of bitterness.
Gordon B. Hinckley

My TALK with God today | **Day** | **Date**

| ☐ Morning Prayer | ☐ Evening Prayer | **ASK IN FAITH** |

| Three Things I am **THANKFUL** for Today: | **What do I need forgiveness for?** |

1.

2.

3.

I turn this over to the Lord. **LET** go and let God handle it

Ask God to help with this challenge today.

Prayer with action makes a difference. I set these intentions for the day:

_____

_____

Ask the Lord to bless these people today.

_____

_____

_____

KEEP communicating with God today

Promptings from the Spirit | **Blessings I received today**

_____ | _____

_____ | _____

_____ | _____

_____ | _____

_____ | _____

Love your enemies, bless them that curse you, do good to them that hate you, and pray for them which despitefully use you, and persecute you. Matthew 5:44

My TALK with God today | **Day** | **Date**

☐   **Morning Prayer**   ☐   **Evening Prayer**

ASK IN FAITH

Three Things I am **THANKFUL** for Today:

1.

2.

3.

I turn this over to the Lord. **LET** go and let God handle it

What do I need forgiveness for?

Ask God to help with this challenge today.

Prayer with action makes a difference. I set these intentions for the day:

_____

_____

_____

_____

_____

Ask the Lord to bless these people today.

KEEP communicating with God today

Promptings from the Spirit   **Blessings I received today**

_____   _____

_____   _____

_____   _____

_____   _____

_____   _____

Mercy unto you, and peace, and love, be multiplied.
Jude 1:2

My TALK with God today → Day | Date

☐ Morning Prayer	☐ Evening Prayer

ASK IN FAITH

Three Things I am **THANKFUL** for Today:	**What do I need forgiveness for?**
1.	
2.	
3.	

I turn this over to the Lord. **LET** go and let God handle it

Ask God to help with this challenge today.

Prayer with action makes a difference. I set these intentions for the day:

_____
_____
_____
_____
_____

Ask the Lord to bless these people today.

KEEP communicating with God today

Promptings from the Spirit	Blessings I received today
_____	_____
_____	_____
_____	_____
_____	_____
_____	_____

Never give up what you want most for what you want today.
Neal A Maxwell

My TALK with God today ➤ **Day**   **Date**

☐ Morning Prayer	☐ Evening Prayer

ASK IN FAITH

Three Things I am **THANKFUL** for Today:
1.
2.
3.

What do I need forgiveness for?

I turn this over to the Lord. **LET** go and let God handle it

Ask God to help with this challenge today.

Prayer with action makes a difference. I set these intentions for the day:

_____

_____

_____

_____

_____

Ask the Lord to bless these people today.

KEEP communicating with God today

Promptings from the Spirit	Blessings I received today
_____	_____
_____	_____
_____	_____
_____	_____
_____	_____

No man can serve two masters: for either he will hate the one, and love the other; or else he will hold to the one, and despise the other. Ye cannot serve God and mammon.
Matthew 6:24

My TALK with God today   **Day**   **Date**

☐ Morning Prayer	☐ Evening Prayer	**ASK IN FAITH**

Three Things I am **THANKFUL** for Today:

1.

2.

3.

I turn this over to the Lord. **LET** go and let God handle it

What do I need forgiveness for?

Ask God to help with this challenge today.

Prayer with action makes a difference. I set these intentions for the day:

_____

_____

_____

_____

_____

Ask the Lord to bless these people today.

KEEP communicating with God today

Promptings from the Spirit	**Blessings I received today**
_____	_____
_____	_____
_____	_____
_____	_____
_____	_____

No man, when he hath lighted a candle, covereth it with a vessel, or putteth it under a bed; but setteth it on a candlestick, that they which enter in may see the light.
Like 8:16

My TALK with God today → **Day**   **Date**

☐ Morning Prayer	☐ Evening Prayer

ASK IN FAITH

What do I need forgiveness for?

Three Things I am **THANKFUL** for Today:

1.

2.

3.

I turn this over to the Lord. **LET** go and let God handle it

Ask God to help with this challenge today.

Prayer with action makes a difference. I set these intentions for the day:

_____

_____

_____

_____

_____

Ask the Lord to bless these people today.

KEEP communicating with God today

Promptings from the Spirit

Blessings I received today

_____ _____

_____ _____

_____ _____

_____ _____

_____

Noble and great. Courageous and determined. Faithful and fearless. That is who you are and who you have always been. And understanding it can change your life, because this knowledge carries a confidence that cannot be duplicated any other way.
Sheri Dew

My TALK with God today	Day	Date

☐ Morning Prayer	☐ Evening Prayer	ASK IN FAITH

Three Things I am **THANKFUL** for Today:

1.

2.

3.

I turn this over to the Lord. **LET** go and let God handle it

Prayer with action makes a difference. I set these intentions for the day:

_____

_____

_____

_____

_____

What do I need forgiveness for?

Ask God to help with this challenge today.

Ask the Lord to bless these people today.

KEEP communicating with God today

Promptings from the Spirit	Blessings I received today
_____	_____
_____	_____
_____	_____
_____	_____
_____	_____

Now faith is the substance of things hoped for, the evidence of things not seen.
Hebrews 11:1

My TALK with God today   **Day**   **Date**

☐ Morning Prayer	☐ Evening Prayer

ASK IN FAITH

Three Things I am **THANKFUL** for Today:

1.

2.

3.

I turn this over to the Lord. **LET** go and let God handle it

What do I need forgiveness for?

Ask God to help with this challenge today.

Prayer with action makes a difference. I set these intentions for the day:

_____

_____

_____

_____

_____

Ask the Lord to bless these people today.

KEEP communicating with God today

Promptings from the Spirit   **Blessings I received today**

_____   _____

_____   _____

_____   _____

_____   _____

_____   _____

Repent all ye ends of the earth, and come unto me, and be baptized in my name, and have faith in me, that ye may be saved.
Moroni 7:34

My TALK with God today → **Day** **Date**

Morning Prayer	Evening Prayer

ASK IN FAITH

Three Things I am **THANKFUL** for Today:
1.
2.
3.

I turn this over to the Lord. **LET** go and let God handle it

What do I need forgiveness for?

Ask God to help with this challenge today.

Prayer with action makes a difference. I set these intentions for the day:

_____

_____

_____

_____

_____

Ask the Lord to bless these people today.

KEEP communicating with God today

Promptings from the Spirit	Blessings I received today
_____	_____
_____	_____
_____	_____
_____	_____
_____	_____

Repent ye therefore, and be converted, that your sins may be blotted out.
Acts 3:19

My TALK with God today   **Day**   **Date**

☐ Morning Prayer	☐ Evening Prayer

ASK IN FAITH

Three Things I am **THANKFUL** for Today:
1.
2.
3.

What do I need forgiveness for?

I turn this over to the Lord. **LET** go and let God handle it

Ask God to help with this challenge today.

Prayer with action makes a difference. I set these intentions for the day:

_____

_____

_____

_____

_____

Ask the Lord to bless these people today.

KEEP communicating with God today

Promptings from the Spirit	Blessings I received today
_____	_____
_____	_____
_____	_____
_____	_____
_____	_____

O Father, look on us today and bless us with thy love. In Jesus' name we humbly pray, O Father up above.
CSB Pg23

My TALK with God today → Day

Date

□ Morning Prayer	□ Evening Prayer

ASK IN FAITH

What do I need forgiveness for?

Three Things I am **THANKFUL** for Today:
1.
2.
3.

I turn this over to the Lord. **LET** go and let God handle it

Ask God to help with this challenge today.

Prayer with action makes a difference. I set these intentions for the day:

_____

_____

_____

_____

_____

Ask the Lord to bless these people today.

KEEP communicating with God today

Promptings from the Spirit	Blessings I received today
_____	_____
_____	_____
_____	_____
_____	_____
_____	_____

O Lord, thou art my God; I will exalt thee, I will praise thy name; for thou hast done wonderful things; thy counsels of old are faithfulness and truth.
Isaiah 25:1

My TALK with God today → **Day** **Date**

☐ Morning Prayer	☐ Evening Prayer

ASK IN FAITH

Three Things I am **THANKFUL** for Today:
1.
2.
3.

What do I need forgiveness for?

I turn this over to the Lord. **LET** go and let God handle it

Ask God to help with this challenge today.

Prayer with action makes a difference. I set these intentions for the day:

_____

_____

_____

_____

_____

Ask the Lord to bless these people today.

KEEP communicating with God today

Promptings from the Spirit	Blessings I received today
_____	_____
_____	_____
_____	_____
_____	_____
_____	_____

O give thanks unto the Lord; for he is good; for his mercy endureth for ever. 1 Chronicles 16:34

My TALK with God today ➤ **Day** **Date**

☐ Morning Prayer ☐ Evening Prayer

ASK IN FAITH

Three Things I am **THANKFUL** for Today:

1.

2.

3.

I turn this over to the Lord. **LET** go and let God handle it

What do I need forgiveness for?

Ask God to help with this challenge today.

Prayer with action makes a difference. I set these intentions for the day:

_____

_____

_____

_____

_____

Ask the Lord to bless these people today.

KEEP communicating with God today

Promptings from the Spirit   Blessings I received today
_____   _____
_____   _____
_____   _____
_____   _____
_____   _____

On occasion we need to make a second effort – and a third effort, and a fourth effort, and as many degrees of effort as may be required to accomplish what we strive to achieve.
Thomas S. Monson

My TALK with God today → **Day**   **Date**

☐ Morning Prayer	☐ Evening Prayer

ASK IN FAITH

What do I need forgiveness for?

Three Things I am **THANKFUL** for Today:
1.
2.
3.

I turn this over to the Lord. **LET** go and let God handle it

Ask God to help with this challenge today.

Prayer with action makes a difference. I set these intentions for the day:

_____

_____

_____

_____

_____

Ask the Lord to bless these people today.

KEEP communicating with God today

Promptings from the Spirit	Blessings I received today
_____	_____
_____	_____
_____	_____
_____	_____
_____	_____

Our religion is "not weight, it is wings." It can carry us through the dark times, the bitter cup. It will be with us in the fiery furnace and the deep pit.
Marion D Hanks

My TALK with God today → **Day**   **Date**

☐ **Morning Prayer**	☐ **Evening Prayer**

ASK IN FAITH

Three Things I am **THANKFUL** for Today:
1.
2.
3.

I turn this over to the Lord. **LET** go and let God handle it

What do I need forgiveness for?

Ask God to help with this challenge today.

Prayer with action makes a difference. I set these intentions for the day:

_____

_____

_____

_____

_____

Ask the Lord to bless these people today.

KEEP communicating with God today

Promptings from the Spirit	**Blessings I received today**
_____	_____
_____	_____
_____	_____
_____	_____
_____	_____

Our Savior, Jesus Christ, knows everything about us we don't want anyone else to know, and He still loves us.
Gerrit W Gong

My TALK with God today   **Day**   **Date**

| ❏ Morning Prayer | ❏ Evening Prayer | **ASK IN FAITH** |

Three Things I am **THANKFUL** for Today:

What do I need forgiveness for?

1.

2.

3.

I turn this over to the Lord. **LET** go and let God handle it

Ask God to help with this challenge today.

Prayer with action makes a difference. I set these intentions for the day:

_____

_____

_____   **Ask the Lord to bless these people today.**

_____

_____

KEEP communicating with God today

Promptings from the Spirit   **Blessings I received today**

_____   _____

_____   _____   Over all these virtues put on love, which binds them all together in perfect unity. Colossians 3:14

_____   _____

_____   _____

_____   _____

My TALK with God today → **Day**

Date

☐ Morning Prayer   ☐ Evening Prayer

ASK IN FAITH

Three Things I am **THANKFUL** for Today:
1.
2.
3.

I turn this over to the Lord. **LET** go and let God handle it

What do I need forgiveness for?

Ask God to help with this challenge today.

Prayer with action makes a difference. I set these intentions for the day:

_____

_____

_____

_____

_____

Ask the Lord to bless these people today.

KEEP communicating with God today

Promptings from the Spirit	Blessings I received today
_____	_____
_____	_____
_____	_____
_____	_____
_____	_____

Peace be unto thy soul; thine adversity and thine afflictions shall be but a small moment. D&C 121:7

My TALK with God today → **Day**   **Date**

☐ Morning Prayer	☐ Evening Prayer

Three Things I am **THANKFUL** for Today:
1.
2.
3.

What do I need forgiveness for?

I turn this over to the Lord. **LET** go and let God handle it

Ask God to help with this challenge today.

Prayer with action makes a difference. I set these intentions for the day:

_____

_____

_____

_____

_____

Ask the Lord to bless these people today.

KEEP communicating with God today

Promptings from the Spirit	Blessings I received today
_____	_____
_____	_____
_____	_____
_____	_____
_____	_____

Peace I leave with you, my peace I give unto you: not as the world giveth, give I unto you. Let not your heart be troubled, neither let it be afraid.
John 14:27

My TALK with God today → **Day**   **Date**

❑ Morning Prayer	❑ Evening Prayer

ASK IN FAITH

Three Things I am **THANKFUL** for Today:

1.

2.

3.

Turn this over to the Lord. **LET** go and let God handle it

What do I need forgiveness for?

Ask God to help with this challenge today.

Prayer with action makes a difference. I set these intentions for the day:

_____

_____

_____

_____

_____

Ask the Lord to bless these people today.

KEEP communicating with God today

Promptings from the Spirit	Blessings I received today
_____	_____
_____	_____
_____	_____
_____	_____
_____	_____

Please listen to the prompting of the Holy Spirit telling you right now, this very moment, that you should accept the atoning gift of the Lord Jesus Christ. Jeffrey R. Holland

My TALK with God today	Day	Date

☐ Morning Prayer ☐ Evening Prayer

ASK IN FAITH

Three Things I am THANKFUL for Today:

1.

2.

3.

What do I need forgiveness for?

Turn this over to the Lord. **LET** go and let God handle it

Ask God to help with this challenge today.

Prayer with action makes a difference. I set these intentions for the day:

_____

_____

_____

_____

_____

Ask the Lord to bless these people today.

KEEP communicating with God today

Promptings from the Spirit	Blessings I received today
_____	_____
_____	_____
_____	_____
_____	_____
_____	_____

Prayer can call down the strength and the revelation that we need to center our thoughts on Jesus Christ and His atoning sacrifice.
Ronald A. Rasband

My TALK with God today   **Day**   **Date**

☐ Morning Prayer	☐ Evening Prayer

ASK IN FAITH

Three Things I am **THANKFUL** for Today:
1.
2.
3.

Turn this over to the Lord. **LET** go and let God handle it

What do I need forgiveness for?

Ask God to help with this challenge today.

Prayer with action makes a difference. I set these intentions for the day:

_____

_____

_____

_____

_____

Ask the Lord to bless these people today.

KEEP communicating with God today

Promptings from the Spirit	Blessings I received today
_____	_____
_____	_____
_____	_____
_____	_____
_____	_____

Reconcile yourselves to the will of God, and not to the will of the devil and the flesh; and remember, after ye are reconciled unto God, that it is only in and through the grace of God that ye are saved. 2 Nephi 10:24

My TALK with God today → **Day** **Date**

☐ Morning Prayer	☐ Evening Prayer

ASK IN FAITH

Three Things I am **THANKFUL** for Today:

1.

2.

3.

Turn this over to the Lord. **LET** go and let God handle it

What do I need forgiveness for?

Ask God to help with this challenge today.

Prayer with action makes a difference. I set these intentions for the day:

_____

_____

_____

_____

_____

Ask the Lord to bless these people today.

KEEP communicating with God today

Promptings from the Spirit	Blessings I received today
_____	_____
_____	_____
_____	_____
_____	_____
_____	_____

Rejoice evermore. Pray without ceasing. In everything give thanks: for this is the will of God in Christ Jesus concerning you. 1 Thessalonians 5:16-18

My TALK with God today ➤ **Day** | **Date**

☐ **Morning Prayer** | ☐ **Evening Prayer**

Three Things I am **THANKFUL** for Today:
1.
2.
3.

Turn this over to the Lord. **LET** go and let God handle it

Prayer with action makes a difference. I set these intentions for the day:

_____

_____

_____

_____

_____

KEEP communicating with God today

Promptings from the Spirit | Blessings I received today
_____ | _____
_____ | _____
_____ | _____
_____ | _____
_____ | _____

ASK IN FAITH

What do I need forgiveness for?

Ask God to help with this challenge today.

Ask the Lord to bless these people today.

Rejoice with them that do rejoice, and weep with them that weep.
Romans 12:15

My TALK with God today → **Day** | **Date**

❑ **Morning Prayer**   ❑ **Evening Prayer** | **ASK IN FAITH**

Three Things I am **THANKFUL** for Today:

1.

2.

3.

Turn this over to the Lord. **LET** go and let God handle it

What do I need forgiveness for?

Ask God to help with this challenge today.

Prayer with action makes a difference. I set these intentions for the day:

_____

_____

_____

_____

_____

Ask the Lord to bless these people today.

KEEP communicating with God today

Promptings from the Spirit | **Blessings I received today**

_____   _____

_____   _____

_____   _____

_____   _____

_____   _____

Rejoiceth not in iniquity, but rejoiceth in the truth; Beareth all things, believeth all things, hopeth all things, endureth all things.
1 Corinthians 13:6-7

My TALK with God today   **Day**   **Date**

☐ **Morning Prayer**   ☐ **Evening Prayer**   **ASK IN FAITH**

Three Things I am **THANKFUL** for Today:

1.

2.

3.

Turn this over to the Lord. **LET** go and let God handle it

What do I need
forgiveness for?

Ask God to help with this
challenge today.

**Prayer with action makes a difference. I set these
intentions for the day:**

_____

_____

_____

_____

_____

Ask the Lord to bless
these people today.

KEEP communicating with God today

Promptings from the Spirit   **Blessings I received today**

_____   _____

_____   _____

_____   _____

_____   _____

_____   _____

Rejoicing in hope;
patient in
tribulation;
continuing instant
in prayer.
Romans 12:12

My TALK with God today | Day | Date

☐ **Morning Prayer** | ☐ **Evening Prayer**

ASK IN FAITH

Three Things I am **THANKFUL** for Today:

1.

2.

3.

Turn this over to the Lord. **LET** go and let God handle it

What do I need forgiveness for?

Ask God to help with this challenge today.

Prayer with action makes a difference. I set these intentions for the day:

_____

_____

_____

_____

_____

Ask the Lord to bless these people today.

KEEP communicating with God today

Promptings from the Spirit | **Blessings I received today**

_____ | _____

_____ | _____

_____ | _____

_____ | _____

_____ | _____

Remember faith, virtue, knowledge, temperance, patience, brotherly kindness, godliness, charity, humility, diligence.
D&C 4:6

My TALK with God today → **Day**   **Date**

☐ **Morning Prayer**	☐ **Evening Prayer**

ASK IN FAITH

Three Things I am **THANKFUL** for Today:

1.

2.

3.

Turn this over to the Lord. **LET** go and let God handle it

What do I need forgiveness for?

Ask God to help with this challenge today.

Prayer with action makes a difference. I set these intentions for the day:

_____

_____

_____

_____

Ask the Lord to bless these people today.

KEEP communicating with God today

Promptings from the Spirit	Blessings I received today
_____	_____
_____	_____
_____	_____
_____	_____
_____	_____

Remember the worth of souls is great in the sight of God.
D&C 18:10

My TALK with God today   **Day**   **Date**

☐ Morning Prayer	☐ Evening Prayer

ASK IN FAITH

Three Things I am **THANKFUL** for Today:

What do I need forgiveness for?

1.

2.

3.

I turn this over to the Lord. **LET** go and let God handle it

Ask God to help with this challenge today.

Prayer with action makes a difference. I set these intentions for the day:

_____
_____
_____
_____
_____

Ask the Lord to bless these people today..

KEEP communicating with God today

Promptings from the Spirit	Blessings I received today
_____	_____
_____	_____
_____	_____
_____	_____
_____	_____

Saith the Lord, turn ye even to me with all your heart, and with fasting, and with weeping, and with mourning.
Joel 2:12

My TALK with God today **Day** **Date**

☐ Morning Prayer	☐ Evening Prayer

ASK IN FAITH

Three Things I am **THANKFUL** for Today:

1.

2.

3.

I turn this over to the Lord. **LET** go and let God handle it

What do I need forgiveness for?

Ask God to help with this challenge today.

Prayer with action makes a difference. I set these intentions for the day:

_____

_____

_____

_____

_____

Ask the Lord to bless these people today..

KEEP communicating with God today

Promptings from the Spirit

_____

_____

_____

_____

_____

Blessings I received today

_____

_____

_____

_____

_____

Salvation is found in no one else, for there is no other name under heaven given to mankind by which we must be saved.
Acts 4:12

My TALK with God today | **Day** | **Date**

☐ **Morning Prayer** | ☐ **Evening Prayer** | **ASK IN FAITH**

Three Things I am **THANKFUL** for Today:

1.

2.

3.

I turn this over to the Lord. **LET** go and let God handle it

What do I need forgiveness for?

Ask God to help with this challenge today.

Prayer with action makes a difference. I set these intentions for the day:

_____

_____

_____

_____

_____

Ask the Lord to bless these people today..

KEEP communicating with God today

Promptings from the Spirit | **Blessings I received today**

_____ | _____

_____ | _____

_____ | _____

_____ | _____

_____ | _____

Savior, may I learn to love thee, walk the path that thou hast shown. Pause to help and lift another, finding strength beyond my own. Savior, may I learn to love thee—Lord, I would follow thee.
Hymn 220

My TALK with God today → **Day**   **Date**

☐ Morning Prayer	☐ Evening Prayer

ASK IN FAITH

Three Things I am **THANKFUL** for Today:

1.

2.

3.

I turn this over to the Lord. **LET** go and let God handle it

What do I need forgiveness for?

Ask God to help with this challenge today.

Prayer with action makes a difference. I set these intentions for the day:

_____

_____

_____

_____

_____

Ask the Lord to bless these people today..

KEEP communicating with God today

Promptings from the Spirit	Blessings I received today
_____	_____
_____	_____
_____	_____
_____	_____
_____	_____

Seek the LORD and his strength; seek his presence continually.
1 Chronicles 16:11

My TALK with God today   **Day**   **Date**

☐ **Morning Prayer**	☐ **Evening Prayer**

ASK IN FAITH

Three Things I am **THANKFUL** for Today:

1.

2.

3.

What do I need forgiveness for?

I turn this over to the Lord. **LET** go and let God handle it

Ask God to help with this challenge today.

Prayer with action makes a difference. I set these intentions for the day:

_____

_____

_____

_____

_____

Ask the Lord to bless these people today..

KEEP communicating with God today

Promptings from the Spirit	**Blessings I received today**
_____	_____
_____	_____
_____	_____
_____	_____
_____	_____

Seek the Lord thy God, thou shalt find him, if thou seek him with all thy heart and with all thy soul. Deuteronomy 4:29

My TALK with God today ➤ **Day** | **Date**

| ☐ Morning Prayer | ☐ Evening Prayer | **ASK IN FAITH** |

Three Things I am **THANKFUL** for Today:

What do I need forgiveness for?

1.

2.

3.

I turn this over to the Lord. **LET** go and let God handle it

Ask God to help with this challenge today.

Prayer with action makes a difference. I set these intentions for the day:

_____

_____

_____   **Ask the Lord to bless these people today..**

_____

_____

KEEP communicating with God today

Promptings from the Spirit   **Blessings I received today**

_____   _____

_____   _____

_____   _____

_____   _____

_____   _____

Set aside time each day to thank the Lord for that day. Never allow yourself to forget, even if it's a quick "thank you for getting me through another day. M. Russell Ballard

My TALK with God today ➡ **Day**   **Date**

☐ Morning Prayer	☐ Evening Prayer

Three Things I am **THANKFUL** for Today:

1.

2.

3.

I turn this over to the Lord. **LET** go and let God handle it

Prayer with action makes a difference. I set these intentions for the day:

_____

_____

_____

_____

_____

ASK IN FAITH

What do I need forgiveness for?

Ask God to help with this challenge today.

Ask the Lord to bless these people today..

KEEP communicating with God today

Promptings from the Spirit	Blessings I received today
_____	_____
_____	_____
_____	_____
_____	_____
_____	_____

So amid the conflict, whether great or small, do not be discouraged; God is over all. Count your many blessings; angels will attend, help and comfort give you to your journey's end.
Hymn 241

My TALK with God today **Day** **Date**

☐ Morning Prayer	☐ Evening Prayer

ASK IN FAITH

Three Things I am **THANKFUL** for Today:

1.

2.

3.

I turn this over to the Lord. **LET** go and let God handle it

What do I need forgiveness for?

Ask God to help with this challenge today.

Prayer with action makes a difference. I set these intentions for the day:

_____

_____

_____

_____

_____

Ask the Lord to bless these people today..

KEEP communicating with God today

Promptings from the Spirit

_____

_____

_____

_____

_____

Blessings I received today

_____

_____

_____

_____

_____

So if you have made covenants, keep them. If you haven't made them, make them. If you have made them and broken them, repent and repair them. It is never too late so long as the Master of the vineyard says there is time.
Jeffrey R. Holland

My TALK with God today | **Day** | **Date**

☐ **Morning Prayer**   ☐ **Evening Prayer**

ASK IN FAITH

Three Things I am **THANKFUL** for Today:

1.

2.

3.

I turn this over to the Lord. **LET** go and let God handle it

What do I need forgiveness for?

Ask God to help with this challenge today.

Prayer with action makes a difference. I set these intentions for the day:

_____

_____

_____

_____

_____

Ask the Lord to bless these people today..

KEEP communicating with God today

Promptings from the Spirit   **Blessings I received today**

_____   _____

_____   _____

_____   _____

_____   _____

_____   _____

Some people will dream big dreams while others will wake up and do them.
John Bytheway

My TALK with God today → **Day** **Date**

☐ Morning Prayer | ☐ Evening Prayer

ASK IN FAITH

Three Things I am **THANKFUL** for Today:

1.

2.

3.

What do I need forgiveness for?

I turn this over to the Lord. **LET** go and let God handle it

Ask God to help with this challenge today.

Prayer with action makes a difference. I set these intentions for the day:

_____

_____

_____

_____

_____

Ask the Lord to bless these people today.

KEEP communicating with God today

Promptings from the Spirit | **Blessings I received today**

_____ | _____

_____ | _____

_____ | _____

_____ | _____

_____ | _____

Submit yourselves therefore to God. Resist the devil, and he will flee from you. James 4:7

My TALK with God today

Day

Date

☐ Morning Prayer	☐ Evening Prayer

Three Things I am **THANKFUL** for Today:

1.

2.

3.

I turn this over to the Lord. **LET** go and let God handle it

Prayer with action makes a difference. I set these intentions for the day:

_____

_____

_____

_____

_____

ASK IN FAITH

What do I need forgiveness for?

Ask God to help with this challenge today.

Ask the Lord to bless these people today.

KEEP communicating with God today

Promptings from the Spirit

_____

_____

_____

_____

_____

Blessings I received today

_____

_____

_____

_____

_____

Thank thee, Father, for this day, for these hours of work and play. For the shining sun above, for thy great and tender love.
CSB Pg24

☐ Morning Prayer	☐ Evening Prayer

ASK IN FAITH

Three Things I am **THANKFUL** for Today:

1.

2.

3.

What do I need forgiveness for?

I turn this over to the Lord. **LET** go and let God handle it

Ask God to help with this challenge today.

Prayer with action makes a difference. I set these intentions for the day:

_____

_____

_____

_____

_____

Ask the Lord to bless these people today.

KEEP communicating with God today

Promptings from the Spirit   **Blessings I received today**

_____   _____

_____   _____

_____   _____

_____   _____

_____   _____

That by him, and through him, and of him, the worlds are and were created, and the inhabitants thereof are begotten sons and daughters unto God.
D&C 76:24

My TALK with God today → **Day**   **Date**

☐ Morning Prayer	☐ Evening Prayer

ASK IN FAITH

Three Things I am **THANKFUL** for Today:

1.

2.

3.

I turn this over to the Lord. **LET** go and let God handle it

What do I need forgiveness for?

Ask God to help with this challenge today.

Prayer with action makes a difference. I set these intentions for the day:

_____

_____

_____

_____

_____

Ask the Lord to bless these people today.

KEEP communicating with God today

Promptings from the Spirit	Blessings I received today
_____	_____
_____	_____
_____	_____
_____	_____
_____	_____

That he would grant you, according to the riches of his glory, to be strengthened with might by his Spirit in the inner man; that Christ may dwell in your hearts by faith; that ye, being rooted and grounded in love. Ephesians 3:16-17

My TALK with God today

Day _____ **Date** _____

☐ **Morning Prayer**   ☐ **Evening Prayer**

Three Things I am **THANKFUL** for Today:
1.
2.
3.

I turn this over to the Lord. **LET** go and let God handle it

Prayer with action makes a difference. I set these intentions for the day:

_____

_____

_____

_____

_____

ASK IN FAITH

What do I need forgiveness for?

Ask God to help with this challenge today.

Ask the Lord to bless these people today.

KEEP communicating with God today

Promptings from the Spirit   **Blessings I received today**

_____   _____

_____   _____

_____   _____

_____   _____

_____   _____

The best antidote I know for worry is work. The best medicine for despair is service. The best cure for weariness is the challenge of helping someone who is even more tired.
Gordon B. Hinckley

My TALK with God today **Day** **Date**

☐ Morning Prayer	☐ Evening Prayer

Three Things I am **THANKFUL** for Today:

1.

2.

3.

I turn this over to the Lord. **LET** go and let God handle it

Prayer with action makes a difference. I set these intentions for the day:

_____

_____

_____

_____

_____

ASK IN FAITH

What do I need forgiveness for?

Ask God to help with this challenge today.

Ask the Lord to bless these people today.

KEEP communicating with God today

Promptings from the Spirit	Blessings I received today
_____	_____
_____	_____
_____	_____
_____	_____
_____	_____

The eyes of your understanding being enlightened; that ye may know what is the hope of his calling, and what the riches of the glory of his inheritance in the saints.
Ephesians 1:18

My TALK with God today   **Day**   **Date**

☐ Morning Prayer	☐ Evening Prayer

ASK IN FAITH

What do I need forgiveness for?

Three Things I am **THANKFUL** for Today:
1.
2.
3.

I turn this over to the Lord. **LET** go and let God handle it

Ask God to help with this challenge today.

Prayer with action makes a difference. I set these intentions for the day:

_____

_____

_____

_____

_____

Ask the Lord to bless these people today.

KEEP communicating with God today

Promptings from the Spirit   **Blessings I received today**

_____   _____

_____   _____

_____   _____

_____   _____

_____   _____

The family is the most important organization in time or in eternity. Our purpose in life is to create for ourselves eternal family units."
Joseph Fielding Smith

My TALK with God today → Day   Date

☐ Morning Prayer	☐ Evening Prayer

ASK IN FAITH

Three Things I am **THANKFUL** for Today:

1.

2.

3.

I turn this over to the Lord. **LET** go and let God handle it

What do I need forgiveness for?

Ask God to help with this challenge today.

Prayer with action makes a difference. I set these intentions for the day:

_____

_____

_____

_____

_____

Ask the Lord to bless these people today.

KEEP communicating with God today

Promptings from the Spirit	Blessings I received today
_____	_____
_____	_____
_____	_____
_____	_____
_____	_____

The formula of faith is to hold on, work on, see it through, and let the distress of earlier hours—real or imagined—fall away in the abundance of the final reward. Don't dwell on old issues or grievances—not toward yourself nor your neighbor nor even, I might add, toward this true and living Church.
Jeffrey R Holland

My TALK with God today → **Day** **Date**

☐ Morning Prayer	☐ Evening Prayer	**ASK IN FAITH**

What do I need forgiveness for?

Three Things I am **THANKFUL** for Today:

1.

2.

3.

I turn this over to the Lord. **LET** go and let God handle it

Ask God to help with this challenge today.

Prayer with action makes a difference. I set these intentions for the day:

_____

_____

Ask the Lord to bless these people today.

_____

_____

_____

KEEP communicating with God today

Promptings from the Spirit	Blessings I received today
_____	_____
_____	_____
_____	_____
_____	_____
_____	

The grace of our Lord Jesus Christ be with you all.
2 Thessalonians 3:18

My TALK with God today   **Day**   **Date**

☐ Morning Prayer	☐ Evening Prayer

ASK IN FAITH

Three Things I am **THANKFUL** for Today:
1.
2.
3.

What do I need forgiveness for?

I turn this over to the Lord. **LET** go and let God handle it

Ask God to help with this challenge today.

Prayer with action makes a difference. I set these intentions for the day:

_____

_____

_____

_____

_____

Ask the Lord to bless these people today.

KEEP communicating with God today

Promptings from the Spirit	Blessings I received today
_____	_____
_____	_____
_____	_____
_____	_____
_____	_____

The grace of our Lord Jesus Christ be with your spirit. Philemon 1:25

My TALK with God today   **Day**   **Date**

☐ **Morning Prayer** | ☐ **Evening Prayer**

| **ASK IN FAITH** |

Three Things I am THANKFUL for Today:

1.

2.

3.

I turn this over to the Lord. **LET** go and let God handle it

What do I need forgiveness for?

Ask God to help with this challenge today.

Prayer with action makes a difference. I set these intentions for the day:

_____

_____

_____

_____

_____

Ask the Lord to bless these people today.

KEEP communicating with God today

Promptings from the Spirit | **Blessings I received today**

_____ | _____

_____ | _____

_____ | _____

_____ | _____

_____ | _____

The grass withereth, the flower fadeth: but the word of our God shall stand for ever.
Isaiah 40:8

My TALK with God today → Day   Date

☐ Morning Prayer	☐ Evening Prayer

ASK IN FAITH

Three Things I am **THANKFUL** for Today:
1.
2.
3.

What do I need
forgiveness for?

I turn this over to the Lord. **LET** go and let God handle it

Ask God to help with this
challenge today.

**Prayer with action makes a difference. I set these
intentions for the day:**

_____

_____

_____

Ask the Lord to bless
these people today.

_____

_____

KEEP communicating with God today

Promptings from the Spirit	Blessings I received today
_____	_____
_____	_____
_____	_____
_____	_____
_____	_____

The greatness of the
world in which we
live is the
accumulated
goodness of many
small and seemingly
inconsequential acts.
Gordon B. Hinckley

My TALK with God today → **Day** **Date**

| ☐ Morning Prayer | ☐ Evening Prayer | **ASK IN FAITH** |

What do I need forgiveness for?

Three Things I am **THANKFUL** for Today:
1.
2.
3.

I turn this over to the Lord. **LET** go and let God handle it

Ask God to help with this challenge today.

Prayer with action makes a difference. I set these intentions for the day:

_____

_____

_____

_____

_____

Ask the Lord to bless these people today.

KEEP communicating with God today

Promptings from the Spirit	Blessings I received today
_____	_____
_____	_____
_____	_____
_____	_____
_____	_____

The heights by great men reached and kept Were not attained by sudden flight, But they, while their companions slept, were toiling upward in the night.
Henry Wadsworth Longfellow

My TALK with God today → **Day**

Date

☐ **Morning Prayer**   ☐ **Evening Prayer**

ASK IN FAITH

Three Things I am **THANKFUL** for Today:

1.

2.

3.

I turn this over to the Lord. **LET** go and let God handle it

What do I need forgiveness for?

Ask God to help with this challenge today.

Prayer with action makes a difference. I set these intentions for the day:

_____

_____

_____

_____

_____

Ask the Lord to bless these people today.

KEEP communicating with God today

Promptings from the Spirit	Blessings I received today
_____	_____
_____	_____
_____	_____
_____	_____
_____	_____

The irony of the Atonement is that it is infinite and eternal, yet it is applied individually, one person at a time.
M. Russell Ballard

My TALK with God today   **Day**   **Date**

☐ Morning Prayer	☐ Evening Prayer

ASK IN FAITH

Three Things I am **THANKFUL** for Today:
1.
2.
3.

I turn this over to the Lord. **LET** go and let God handle it

What do I need forgiveness for?

Ask God to help with this challenge today.

Prayer with action makes a difference. I set these intentions for the day:

_____

_____

_____

_____

_____

Ask the Lord to bless these people today.

KEEP communicating with God today

Promptings from the Spirit	Blessings I received today
_____	_____
_____	_____
_____	_____
_____	_____
_____	_____

The Lord does not expect us to do more than we can do, but He does expect us to do what we can do, when we can do it.
W. Christopher Waddell

My TALK with God today → **Day**

Date

☐ **Morning Prayer**	☐ **Evening Prayer**

ASK IN FAITH

What do I need forgiveness for?

Three Things I am **THANKFUL** for Today:

1.

2.

3.

I turn this over to the Lord. **LET** go and let God handle it

Ask God to help with this challenge today.

Prayer with action makes a difference. I set these intentions for the day:

_____

_____

_____

_____

_____

Ask the Lord to bless these people today.

KEEP communicating with God today

Promptings from the Spirit

Blessings I received today

_____ _____

_____ _____

_____ _____

_____ _____

_____ _____

The Lord is good, a strong hold in the day of trouble; and he knoweth them that trust in him. Nahum 1:7

My TALK with God today →　Day　　　　　　　Date

☐ Morning Prayer	☐ Evening Prayer

ASK IN FAITH

What do I need forgiveness for?

Three Things I am **THANKFUL** for Today:
1.
2.
3.

I turn this over to the Lord. **LET** go and let God handle it

Ask God to help with this challenge today.

Prayer with action makes a difference. I set these intentions for the day:

_____
_____
_____
_____
_____

Ask the Lord to bless these people today.

KEEP communicating with God today

Promptings from the Spirit	Blessings I received today
_____	_____
_____	_____
_____	_____
_____	_____
_____	_____

The Lord is merciful and gracious, slow to anger, and plenteous in mercy.
Psalms 103:8

My TALK with God today **Day** **Date**

☐ **Morning Prayer**	☐ **Evening Prayer**

ASK IN FAITH

Three Things I am **THANKFUL** for Today:
1.
2.
3.

What do I need forgiveness for?

I turn this over to the Lord. **LET** go and let God handle it

Ask God to help with this challenge today.

Prayer with action makes a difference. I set these intentions for the day:

_____

_____

_____

_____

_____

Ask the Lord to bless these people today.

KEEP communicating with God today

Promptings from the Spirit	Blessings I received today
_____	_____
_____	_____
_____	_____
_____	_____
_____	_____

The Lord is on my side; I will not fear.
Psalms 118:6

My TALK with God today　　　**Day**　　　　　　　**Date**

☐　**Morning Prayer**	☐　**Evening Prayer**

ASK IN FAITH

What do I need forgiveness for?

Three Things I am **THANKFUL** for Today:
1.
2.
3.

Turn this over to the Lord. **LET** go and let God handle it

Ask God to help with this challenge today.

Prayer with action makes a difference. I set these intentions for the day:

_____

_____

_____

_____

_____

Ask the Lord to bless these people today.

KEEP communicating with God today

Promptings from the Spirit	Blessings I received today
_____	_____
_____	_____
_____	_____
_____	_____
_____	_____

The Lord is with us, mindful of us and blessing us in ways only He can do.
Ronald A. Rasband

My TALK with God today　　**Day**　　　　　　　**Date**

☐ Morning Prayer	☐ Evening Prayer

ASK IN FAITH

Three Things I am **THANKFUL** for Today:
1.
2.
3.

What do I need forgiveness for?

Turn this over to the Lord. **LET** go and let God handle it

Ask God to help with this challenge today.

Prayer with action makes a difference. I set these intentions for the day:

_____

_____

_____

_____

_____

Ask the Lord to bless these people today.

KEEP communicating with God today

Promptings from the Spirit	Blessings I received today
_____	_____
_____	_____
_____	_____
_____	_____
_____	_____

The only thing you have 100% control over is you.
Hyrum W. Smith

My TALK with God today → **Day** **Date**

☐ Morning Prayer	☐ Evening Prayer

ASK IN FAITH

Three Things I am **THANKFUL** for Today:

1.

2.

3.

Turn this over to the Lord. **LET** go and let God handle it

What do I need forgiveness for?

Ask God to help with this challenge today.

Prayer with action makes a difference. I set these intentions for the day:

_____

_____

_____

_____

_____

Ask the Lord to bless these people today.

KEEP communicating with God today

Promptings from the Spirit   Blessings I received today

_____   _____

_____   _____

_____   _____

_____   _____

_____   _____

The only way to get through life is to laugh your way through it. You either have to laugh or cry. I prefer to laugh. Crying gives me a headache.
Majorie Pay Hinckley

My TALK with God today → **Day**   **Date**

☐ Morning Prayer	☐ Evening Prayer

ASK IN FAITH

Three Things I am **THANKFUL** for Today:

1.

2.

3.

What do I need forgiveness for?

Turn this over to the Lord. **LET** go and let God handle it

Ask God to help with this challenge today.

Prayer with action makes a difference. I set these intentions for the day:

_____

_____

_____

_____

_____

Ask the Lord to bless these people today.

KEEP communicating with God today

Promptings from the Spirit	Blessings I received today
_____	_____
_____	_____
_____	_____
_____	_____
_____	_____

The principles of living greatly include the capacity to face trouble with courage, disappointment with cheerfulness, and trial with humility.
Thomas S. Monson

My TALK with God today → **Day**   **Date**

☐ **Morning Prayer**	☐ **Evening Prayer**

ASK IN FAITH

Three Things I am **THANKFUL** for Today:
1.
2.
3.

What do I need forgiveness for?

Turn this over to the Lord. **LET** go and let God handle it

Ask God to help with this challenge today.

Prayer with action makes a difference. I set these intentions for the day:

_____

_____

_____

_____

_____

Ask the Lord to bless these people today.

KEEP communicating with God today

Promptings from the Spirit	Blessings I received today
_____	_____
_____	_____
_____	_____
_____	_____
_____	_____

The race we are really in is the race against sin, and surely envy is one of the most universal of those.
Jeffrey R. Holland

My TALK with God today · **Day** · **Date**

❏ **Morning Prayer**   ❏ **Evening Prayer**

ASK IN FAITH

Three Things I am **THANKFUL** for Today:
1.
2.
3.

What do I need forgiveness for?

Turn this over to the Lord. **LET** go and let God handle it

Ask God to help with this challenge today.

Prayer with action makes a difference. I set these intentions for the day:

_____

_____

Ask the Lord to bless these people today.

_____

_____

KEEP communicating with God today

Promptings from the Spirit	**Blessings I received today**
_____	_____
_____	_____
_____	_____
_____	_____

The Spirit most often communicates as a feeling. You feel it in words that are familiar to you, that make sense to you, that prompt you. Ronald A. Rasband

My TALK with God today   **Day**   **Date**

☐ **Morning Prayer**	☐ **Evening Prayer**	**ASK IN FAITH**

Three Things I am **THANKFUL** for Today:

1.

2.

3.

Turn this over to the Lord. **LET** go and let God handle it

What do I need forgiveness for?

Prayer with action makes a difference. I set these intentions for the day:

_____

_____

_____

_____

_____

Ask God to help with this challenge today.

Ask the Lord to bless these people today.

KEEP communicating with God today

Promptings from the Spirit   **Blessings I received today**

_____   _____

_____   _____

_____   _____

_____   _____

_____   _____

The things which are impossible with men are possible with God.
Luke 18:27

My TALK with God today	Day	Date

☐ Morning Prayer	☐ Evening Prayer	**ASK IN FAITH**

Three Things I am **THANKFUL** for Today:

1.

2.

3.

Turn this over to the Lord. **LET** go and let God handle it

What do I need forgiveness for?

Ask God to help with this challenge today.

Prayer with action makes a difference. I set these intentions for the day:

_____

_____

_____

_____

_____

Ask the Lord to bless these people today.

KEEP communicating with God today

Promptings from the Spirit	Blessings I received today
_____	_____
_____	_____
_____	_____
_____	_____
_____	_____

Then shall ye call upon me, and ye shall go and pray unto me, and I will hearken unto you.
Jeremiah 29:12

My TALK with God today → **Day** | **Date**

☐ Morning Prayer	☐ Evening Prayer

ASK IN FAITH

What do I need forgiveness for?

Three Things I am **THANKFUL** for Today:

1.

2.

3.

Turn this over to the Lord. **LET** go and let God handle it

Ask God to help with this challenge today.

Prayer with action makes a difference. I set these intentions for the day:

_____

_____

_____

_____

_____

Ask the Lord to bless these people today.

KEEP communicating with God today

Promptings from the Spirit	Blessings I received today
_____	_____
_____	_____
_____	_____
_____	_____
_____	_____

There are chances for work all around just now, opportunities right in our way. Do not let them pass by, saying, Sometime I'll try, but go and do something today.
Hymn 223

My TALK with God today → Day   Date

☐ Morning Prayer   ☐ Evening Prayer

ASK IN FAITH

Three Things I am **THANKFUL** for Today:

1.

2.

3.

I turn this over to the Lord. **LET** go and let God handle it

What do I need forgiveness for?

Ask God to help with this challenge today.

Prayer with action makes a difference. I set these intentions for the day:

_____

_____

_____

_____

_____

Ask the Lord to bless these people today..

KEEP communicating with God today

Promptings from the Spirit

_____

_____

_____

_____

_____

Blessings I received today

_____

_____

_____

_____

_____

There are going to be times in our lives when someone else gets an unexpected blessing or receives some special recognition. May I plead with us not to be hurt—and certainly not to feel envious—when good fortune comes to another person?
Jeffrey R. Holland

My TALK with God today **Day** **Date**

☐ Morning Prayer	☐ Evening Prayer

| | **ASK IN FAITH** |

Three Things I am **THANKFUL** for Today:

What do I need forgiveness for?

1.

2.

3.

I turn this over to the Lord. **LET** go and let God handle it

Ask God to help with this challenge today.

Prayer with action makes a difference. I set these intentions for the day:

_____

_____

Ask the Lord to bless these people today..

_____

_____

_____

KEEP communicating with God today

Promptings from the Spirit	**Blessings I received today**
_____	_____
_____	_____
_____	_____
_____	_____
_____	_____

There is no chance, no fate, no destiny that can circumvent, or hinder, or control the firm resolve of a determined soul.
Hyrum W. Smith

My TALK with God today | **Day** | **Date**

☐ Morning Prayer	☐ Evening Prayer

Three Things I am **THANKFUL** for Today:

1.

2.

3.

I turn this over to the Lord. **LET** go and let God handle it

Prayer with action makes a difference. I set these intentions for the day:

_____

_____

_____

_____

_____

ASK IN FAITH

What do I need forgiveness for?

Ask God to help with this challenge today.

Ask the Lord to bless these people today..

KEEP communicating with God today

Promptings from the Spirit | **Blessings I received today**

_____ | _____

_____ | _____

_____ | _____

_____ | _____

_____ | _____

There is one body, and one Spirit, even as ye are called in one hope of your calling. Ephesians 4:4

My TALK with God today → **Day** **Date**

☐ **Morning Prayer**	☐ **Evening Prayer**

ASK IN FAITH

Three Things I am **THANKFUL** for Today:

1.

2.

3.

I turn this over to the Lord. **LET** go and let God handle it

What do I need forgiveness for?

Ask God to help with this challenge today.

Prayer with action makes a difference. I set these intentions for the day:

_____

_____

_____

_____

_____

Ask the Lord to bless these people today..

KEEP communicating with God today

Promptings from the Spirit	Blessings I received today
_____	_____
_____	_____
_____	_____
_____	_____
_____	_____

There is one thing the power of God and the power of Satan have in common: Neither can influence us unless we allow them to.
Sheri Dew

My TALK with God today → **Day** **Date**

☐ Morning Prayer	☐ Evening Prayer

ASK IN FAITH

Three Things I am **THANKFUL** for Today:
1.
2.
3.

What do I need forgiveness for?

I turn this over to the Lord. **LET** go and let God handle it

Ask God to help with this challenge today.

Prayer with action makes a difference. I set these intentions for the day:

_____

_____

_____

_____

_____

Ask the Lord to bless these people today..

KEEP communicating with God today

Promptings from the Spirit	Blessings I received today
_____	_____
_____	_____
_____	_____
_____	_____
_____	_____

There is no problem which you cannot overcome. There is no dream that in the unfolding of time and eternity cannot yet be realized.
Jeffrey R. Holland

My TALK with God today   **Day**   **Date**

☐ Morning Prayer	☐ Evening Prayer

ASK IN FAITH

What do I need forgiveness for?

Three Things I am **THANKFUL** for Today:

1.

2.

3.

I turn this over to the Lord. **LET** go and let God handle it

Ask God to help with this challenge today.

Prayer with action makes a difference. I set these intentions for the day:

_____

_____

_____   **Ask the Lord to bless these people today..**

_____

_____

KEEP communicating with God today

Promptings from the Spirit	Blessings I received today
_____	_____
_____	_____
_____	_____
_____	_____
_____	_____

There let the way appear, steps unto heaven; All that thou sendest me, In mercy given; Angels to beckon me Nearer, my God, to thee. Hymn 100

| **My TALK with God today** | **Day** | **Date** |

| ☐ **Morning Prayer** | ☐ **Evening Prayer** |

ASK IN FAITH

Three Things I am **THANKFUL** for Today:

1.

2.

3.

I turn this over to the Lord. **LET** go and let God handle it

What do I need forgiveness for?

Prayer with action makes a difference. I set these intentions for the day:

_____

_____

_____

_____

_____

Ask God to help with this challenge today.

Ask the Lord to bless these people today..

KEEP communicating with God today

Promptings from the Spirit

_____

_____

_____

_____

_____

Blessings I received today

_____

_____

_____

_____

_____

Therefore I say unto you, What things soever ye desire, when ye pray, believe that ye receive them, and ye shall have them. Mark 11:24

My TALK with God today   **Day**   **Date**

☐ Morning Prayer	☐ Evening Prayer

<table>
<tr><td colspan="2">Three Things I am THANKFUL for Today:</td></tr>
<tr><td>1.</td></tr>
<tr><td>2.</td></tr>
<tr><td>3.</td></tr>
</table>

I turn this over to the Lord. **LET** go and let God handle it

Prayer with action makes a difference. I set these intentions for the day:

_____

_____

_____

_____

_____

KEEP communicating with God today

Promptings from the Spirit	Blessings I received today
_____	_____
_____	_____
_____	_____
_____	_____
_____	_____

ASK IN FAITH

What do I need forgiveness for?

Ask God to help with this challenge today.

Ask the Lord to bless these people today..

Therefore, as God's chosen people, holy and dearly loved, clothe yourselves with compassion, kindness, humility, gentleness and patience.
Colossians 3:12

My TALK with God today **Day** **Date**

☐ **Morning Prayer** ☐ **Evening Prayer**

Three Things I am **THANKFUL** for Today:

1.

2.

3.

I turn this over to the Lord. **LET** go and let God handle it

What do I need forgiveness for?

Ask God to help with this challenge today.

Prayer with action makes a difference. I set these intentions for the day:

_____

_____

_____

_____

_____

Ask the Lord to bless these people today..

KEEP communicating with God today

Promptings from the Spirit **Blessings I received today**

_____ _____

_____ _____

_____ _____

_____ _____

_____ _____

Therefore, my beloved brethren, be ye steadfast, unmovable, always abounding in the work of the Lord, forasmuch as ye know that your labor is not in vain in the Lord.
1 Corinthians 15:58

My TALK with God today → **Day**   **Date**

☐ Morning Prayer	☐ Evening Prayer

ASK IN FAITH

Three Things I am **THANKFUL** for Today:
1.
2.
3.

What do I need forgiveness for?

I turn this over to the Lord. **LET** go and let God handle it

Ask God to help with this challenge today.

Prayer with action makes a difference. I set these intentions for the day:

_____

_____

_____

_____

_____

Ask the Lord to bless these people today.

KEEP communicating with God today

Promptings from the Spirit	Blessings I received today
_____	_____
_____	_____
_____	_____
_____	_____
_____	_____

They had waxed strong in the knowledge of the truth; for they were men of sound understanding and they had searched the scriptures diligently, that they might know the word of God.
Alma 17:2

My TALK with God today | **Day** | **Date**

| ☐ Morning Prayer | ☐ Evening Prayer |

ASK IN FAITH

| Three Things I am **THANKFUL** for Today: |
| 1. |
| 2. |
| 3. |

I turn this over to the Lord. **LET** go and let God handle it

What do I need forgiveness for?

Prayer with action makes a difference. I set these intentions for the day:

_____

_____

_____

_____

_____

Ask God to help with this challenge today.

Ask the Lord to bless these people today.

KEEP communicating with God today

Promptings from the Spirit	Blessings I received today
_____	_____
_____	_____
_____	_____
_____	_____
_____	_____

Those who fail to keep their goals in mind and fail to discipline themselves find that they are following detours and paths that lead to failure and destruction.
N Eldon Tanner

My TALK with God today → **Day**   **Date**

| ☐ **Morning Prayer** | ☐ **Evening Prayer** | **ASK IN FAITH** |

Three Things I am THANKFUL for Today:

1.

2.

3.

What do I need forgiveness for?

I turn this over to the Lord. **LET** go and let God handle it

Ask God to help with this challenge today.

Prayer with action makes a difference. I set these intentions for the day:

_____

_____

_____

_____

_____

Ask the Lord to bless these people today.

KEEP communicating with God today

Promptings from the Spirit   **Blessings I received today**

_____   _____

_____   _____

_____   _____

_____   _____

_____   _____

Thou shalt keep therefore his statutes, and his commandments, which I command thee this day, that it may go well with thee, and with thy children after thee, and that thou mayest prolong thy days upon the earth, which the Lord thy God giveth thee, for ever.
Deuteronomy 4:40

My TALK with God today ➤ **Day** **Date**

☐ **Morning Prayer** ☐ **Evening Prayer**

ASK IN FAITH

Three Things I am **THANKFUL** for Today:
1.
2.
3.

What do I need forgiveness for?

I turn this over to the Lord. **LET** go and let God handle it

Ask God to help with this challenge today.

Prayer with action makes a difference. I set these intentions for the day:

_____

_____

_____

_____

_____

Ask the Lord to bless these people today.

KEEP communicating with God today

Promptings from the Spirit   **Blessings I received today**

_____   _____

_____   _____

_____   _____

_____   _____

_____   _____

Thou shalt love thy neighbor as thyself.
Mark 12:31

My TALK with God today	Day	Date

☐ Morning Prayer	☐ Evening Prayer

ASK IN FAITH

What do I need forgiveness for?

Three Things I am **THANKFUL** for Today:

1.

2.

3.

I turn this over to the Lord. **LET** go and let God handle it

Ask God to help with this challenge today.

Prayer with action makes a difference. I set these intentions for the day:

_____

_____

Ask the Lord to bless these people today.

_____

_____

_____

KEEP communicating with God today

Promptings from the Spirit	Blessings I received today
_____	_____
_____	_____
_____	_____
_____	_____
_____	_____

Through Jesus Christ, we are given the strength to make lasting changes. As we humbly turn to Him, He will increase our capacity to change.
Becky Craven

My TALK with God today | **Day** | **Date**

☐ Morning Prayer	☐ Evening Prayer

ASK IN FAITH

Three Things I am **THANKFUL** for Today:

1.

2.

3.

What do I need forgiveness for?

I turn this over to the Lord. **LET** go and let God handle it

Ask God to help with this challenge today.

Prayer with action makes a difference. I set these intentions for the day:

_____

_____

_____

_____

_____

Ask the Lord to bless these people today.

KEEP communicating with God today

Promptings from the Spirit	**Blessings I received today**
_____	_____
_____	_____
_____	_____
_____	_____
_____	_____

Through our Savior Jesus Christ, we can all be mended, made whole and fulfill our purpose.
Cristina B. Franco

My TALK with God today → Day   Date

☐ Morning Prayer	☐ Evening Prayer

ASK IN FAITH

What do I need forgiveness for?

Three Things I am **THANKFUL** for Today:
1.
2.
3.

I turn this over to the Lord. **LET** go and let God handle it

Ask God to help with this challenge today.

Prayer with action makes a difference. I set these intentions for the day:

_____

_____

_____

_____

_____

Ask the Lord to bless these people today.

KEEP communicating with God today

Promptings from the Spirit	Blessings I received today
_____	_____
_____	_____
_____	_____
_____	_____
_____	_____

To any who may be struggling to see that light and find that hope, I say: Hold on. Keep trying. God loves you. Things will improve.
Jeffrey R. Holland

My TALK with God today ➤ **Day**   **Date**

☐ **Morning Prayer**   ☐ **Evening Prayer**

ASK IN FAITH

Three Things I am **THANKFUL** for Today:

1.

2.

3.

What do I need forgiveness for?

I turn this over to the Lord. **LET** go and let God handle it

Ask God to help with this challenge today.

Prayer with action makes a difference. I set these intentions for the day:

_____

_____

_____

_____

_____

Ask the Lord to bless these people today.

KEEP communicating with God today

Promptings from the Spirit   **Blessings I received today**

_____   _____

_____   _____

_____   _____

_____   _____

_____   _____

Truly, for those with faithful hearts and eyes to see, the Lord's tender mercies are manifest amidst life's challenges.
Gerrit W. Gong

My TALK with God today ➤ **Day**   **Date**

☐ Morning Prayer	☐ Evening Prayer

ASK IN FAITH

Three Things I am **THANKFUL** for Today:
1.
2.
3.

What do I need forgiveness for?

I turn this over to the Lord. **LET** go and let God handle it

Ask God to help with this challenge today.

Prayer with action makes a difference. I set these intentions for the day:

_____

_____

_____

_____

_____

Ask the Lord to bless these people today.

KEEP communicating with God today

Promptings from the Spirit	Blessings I received today
_____	_____
_____	_____
_____	_____
_____	_____
_____	_____

Verily, verily, I say unto you, if you desire a further witness, cast your mind upon the night that you cried unto me in your heart, that you might know concerning the truth of these things.
D&C 6:22

My TALK with God today   **Day**   **Date**

☐ Morning Prayer	☐ Evening Prayer

ASK IN FAITH

Three Things I am **THANKFUL** for Today:
1.
2.
3.

What do I need forgiveness for?

I turn this over to the Lord. **LET** go and let God handle it

Ask God to help with this challenge today.

Prayer with action makes a difference. I set these intentions for the day:

_____

_____

_____

_____

_____

Ask the Lord to bless these people today.

KEEP communicating with God today

Promptings from the Spirit	Blessings I received today
_____	_____
_____	_____
_____	_____
_____	_____
_____	_____

Waiting upon the Lord implies action. I have learned over the years that our hope in Christ increases when we serve others. Serving as Jesus served, we naturally increase our hope in Him.
M Russell Ballard

My TALK with God today ➤ **Day**   **Date**

☐ Morning Prayer	☐ Evening Prayer

ASK IN FAITH

What do I need forgiveness for?

Three Things I am **THANKFUL** for Today:

1.

2.

3.

I turn this over to the Lord. **LET** go and let God handle it

Ask God to help with this challenge today.

Prayer with action makes a difference. I set these intentions for the day:

_____

_____

_____

_____

_____

Ask the Lord to bless these people today.

KEEP communicating with God today

Promptings from the Spirit	Blessings I received today
_____	_____
_____	_____
_____	_____
_____	_____
_____	_____

Watch and pray, that ye enter not into temptation: the spirit indeed is willing, but the flesh is weak. Matthew 26:41

My TALK with God today → **Day**   **Date**

☐ Morning Prayer	☐ Evening Prayer

ASK IN FAITH

Three Things I am **THANKFUL** for Today:
1.
2.
3.

What do I need forgiveness for?

I turn this over to the Lord. **LET** go and let God handle it

Ask God to help with this challenge today.

Prayer with action makes a difference. I set these intentions for the day:

_____
_____
_____
_____
_____

Ask the Lord to bless these people today.

KEEP communicating with God today

Promptings from the Spirit	Blessings I received today
_____	_____
_____	_____
_____	_____
_____	_____
_____	_____

Watch therefore: for ye know not what hour your Lord doth come.
Matthew 24:42

My TALK with God today   Day   Date

ASK IN FAITH

Three Things I am **THANKFUL** for Today:

1.

2.

3.

What do I need forgiveness for?

I turn this over to the Lord. **LET** go and let God handle it

Ask God to help with this challenge today.

Prayer with action makes a difference. I set these intentions for the day:

_____

_____

Ask the Lord to bless these people today.

_____

_____

_____

KEEP communicating with God today

Promptings from the Spirit   **Blessings I received today**

_____   _____

_____   _____

_____   _____

_____   _____

_____   _____

Watch ye, stand fast in the faith, quit you like men, be strong.
1 Corinthians 16:13

My TALK with God today → Day   Date

☐ Morning Prayer | ☐ Evening Prayer

ASK IN FAITH

Three Things I am **THANKFUL** for Today:

1.

2.

3.

What do I need
forgiveness for?

I turn this over to the Lord. **LET** go and let God handle it

Ask God to help with this
challenge today.

**Prayer with action makes a difference. I set these
intentions for the day:**

_____

_____

_____

_____

_____

Ask the Lord to bless
these people today.

KEEP communicating with God today

Promptings from the Spirit | Blessings I received today
_____ | _____
_____ | _____
_____ | _____
_____ | _____
_____ | _____

We are all enlisted till
the conflict is o'er;
Happy are we! Happy
are we! Soldiers in the
army, there's a bright
crown in store; We shall
win and wear it
by and by.
Hymn 250

My TALK with God today → **Day**   **Date**

☐ Morning Prayer	☐ Evening Prayer

ASK IN FAITH

What do I need forgiveness for?

Three Things I am **THANKFUL** for Today:
1.
2.
3.

I turn this over to the Lord. **LET** go and let God handle it

Ask God to help with this challenge today.

Prayer with action makes a difference. I set these intentions for the day:

_____

_____

_____

_____

_____

Ask the Lord to bless these people today.

KEEP communicating with God today

Promptings from the Spirit	Blessings I received today
_____	_____
_____	_____
_____	_____
_____	_____
_____	_____

We are witnesses of these things, and so is the Holy Spirit, whom God has given to those who obey him.
Acts 5:32

My TALK with God today   **Day**   **Date**

☐ **Morning Prayer**	☐ **Evening Prayer**

ASK IN FAITH

What do I need forgiveness for?

Three Things I am **THANKFUL** for Today:
1.
2.
3.

I turn this over to the Lord. **LET** go and let God handle it

Ask God to help with this challenge today.

Prayer with action makes a difference. I set these intentions for the day:

_____

_____

_____

_____

Ask the Lord to bless these people today.

KEEP communicating with God today

Promptings from the Spirit	**Blessings I received today**
_____	_____
_____	_____
_____	_____
_____	_____
_____	

We have direct access to our own revelation so the Lord can comfort and guide us personally.
Milton Camargo

My TALK with God today → Day

Date

- ☐ **Morning Prayer**
- ☐ **Evening Prayer**

ASK IN FAITH

Three Things I am **THANKFUL** for Today:
1.
2.
3.

I turn this over to the Lord. **LET** go and let God handle it

What do I need forgiveness for?

Ask God to help with this challenge today.

Prayer with action makes a difference. I set these intentions for the day:

_____

_____

_____

_____

_____

Ask the Lord to bless these people today.

KEEP communicating with God today

Promptings from the Spirit	Blessings I received today
_____	_____
_____	_____
_____	_____
_____	_____
_____	_____

We learn perfection is in Jesus Christ, not in the perfectionism of the world. Unreal and unrealistic, the world's "insta-perfect" filtered perfectionism can make us feel inadequate, captive to swipes, likes, or double taps.
Gerrit W Gong

My TALK with God today   Day   Date

❑ Morning Prayer	❑ Evening Prayer

ASK IN FAITH

Three Things I am **THANKFUL** for Today:
1.
2.
3.

I turn this over to the Lord. **LET** go and let God handle it

What do I need forgiveness for?

Ask God to help with this challenge today.

Prayer with action makes a difference. I set these intentions for the day:

_____

_____

_____

_____

_____

Ask the Lord to bless these people today.

KEEP communicating with God today

Promptings from the Spirit	Blessings I received today
_____	_____
_____	_____
_____	_____
_____	_____
_____	_____

We must be confident in our first promptings. Sometimes we rationalize; we wonder if we are feeling a spiritual impression or if it is just our own thoughts. When we begin to second-guess, even third-guess, our feelings—and we all have—we are dismissing the Spirit; we are questioning divine counsel.
Ronald A. Rasband

| My TALK with God today | Day | Date |

| ☐ **Morning Prayer** | ☐ **Evening Prayer** |

ASK IN FAITH

Three Things I am **THANKFUL** for Today:

1.

2.

3.

Turn this over to the Lord. **LET** go and let God handle it

What do I need forgiveness for?

Ask God to help with this challenge today.

Prayer with action makes a difference. I set these intentions for the day:

_____

_____

_____

_____

_____

Ask the Lord to bless these people today.

KEEP communicating with God today

Promptings from the Spirit

_____

_____

_____

_____

Blessings I received today

_____

_____

_____

_____

We must be on the job all the time guarding against evil. We must never relax or forget who we are and what we are trying to accomplish.
N Eldon Tanner

My TALK with God today   **Day**   **Date**

☐ **Morning Prayer**	☐ **Evening Prayer**

ASK IN FAITH

Three Things I am **THANKFUL** for Today:

1.

2.

3.

Turn this over to the Lord. **LET** go and let God handle it

What do I need forgiveness for?

Ask God to help with this challenge today.

Prayer with action makes a difference. I set these intentions for the day:

_____

_____

_____

_____

_____

Ask the Lord to bless these people today.

KEEP communicating with God today

Promptings from the Spirit	**Blessings I received today**
_____	_____
_____	_____
_____	_____
_____	_____
_____	_____

We no longer have the luxury of spending our energy on anything that does not lead us and our families to Christ.
Sheri Dew

My TALK with God today → **Day**   **Date**

❑ Morning Prayer	❑ Evening Prayer

ASK IN FAITH

Three Things I am **THANKFUL** for Today:

1.

2.

3.

Turn this over to the Lord. **LET** go and let God handle it

What do I need forgiveness for?

Ask God to help with this challenge today.

Prayer with action makes a difference. I set these intentions for the day:

_____

_____

_____

_____

Ask the Lord to bless these people today.

KEEP communicating with God today

Promptings from the Spirit

_____

_____

_____

_____

_____

Blessings I received today

_____

_____

_____

_____

_____

We often think of substance in terms of food or money, but perhaps what we all need more of in our ministering is mercy.
Sharon Eubank

My TALK with God today	Day	Date

☐ Morning Prayer	☐ Evening Prayer

ASK IN FAITH

What do I need forgiveness for?

Three Things I am **THANKFUL** for Today:

1.

2.

3.

Turn this over to the Lord. **LET** go and let God handle it

Ask God to help with this challenge today.

Prayer with action makes a difference. I set these intentions for the day:

_____

_____

_____

_____

_____

Ask the Lord to bless these people today.

KEEP communicating with God today

Promptings from the Spirit	Blessings I received today
_____	_____
_____	_____
_____	_____
_____	_____
_____	_____

We seek daily to follow Jesus Christ with faith unto repentance and enduring joy.
Gerrit W Gong

My TALK with God today   **Day**   **Date**

❑ Morning Prayer	❑ Evening Prayer

ASK IN FAITH

Three Things I am **THANKFUL** for Today:

1.

2.

3.

Turn this over to the Lord. **LET** go and let God handle it

What do I need forgiveness for?

Ask God to help with this challenge today.

Prayer with action makes a difference. I set these intentions for the day:

_____

_____

_____

_____

_____

Ask the Lord to bless these people today.

KEEP communicating with God today

Promptings from the Spirit   **Blessings I received today**

_____   _____

_____   _____

_____   _____

_____   _____

_____   _____

We tend to become like those whom we admire.
Thomas S. Monson

My TALK with God today **Day** **Date**

☐ **Morning Prayer** ☐ **Evening Prayer**

ASK IN FAITH

Three Things I am **THANKFUL** for Today:

1.

2.

3.

Turn this over to the Lord. **LET** go and let God handle it

What do I need forgiveness for?

Ask God to help with this challenge today.

Prayer with action makes a difference. I set these intentions for the day:

_____

_____

_____

_____

_____

Ask the Lord to bless these people today.

KEEP communicating with God today

Promptings from the Spirit

Blessings I received today

_____ _____

_____ _____

_____ _____

_____ _____

_____ _____

We wage no common war, Cope with no common foe. The enemy's awake; Who's on the Lord's side? Who? Hymn 260

My TALK with God today   **Day**   **Date**

☐ Morning Prayer	☐ Evening Prayer

ASK IN FAITH

Three Things I am **THANKFUL** for Today:

1.

2.

3.

Turn this over to the Lord. **LET** go and let God handle it

What do I need forgiveness for?

Ask God to help with this challenge today.

Prayer with action makes a difference. I set these intentions for the day:

_____

_____

_____

_____

_____

Ask the Lord to bless these people today.

KEEP communicating with God today

Promptings from the Spirit

_____

_____

_____

_____

_____

Blessings I received today

_____

_____

_____

_____

_____

We're not alone--at least, we're alone only if we choose to be alone. We're alone only if we choose to go through life relying solely on our own strength rather than learning to draw upon the power of God.
Sherri Dew

My TALK with God today   **Day**   **Date**

☐ Morning Prayer	☐ Evening Prayer

ASK IN FAITH

Three Things I am **THANKFUL** for Today:

1.

2.

3.

Turn this over to the Lord. **LET** go and let God handle it

What do I need forgiveness for?

Ask God to help with this challenge today.

Prayer with action makes a difference. I set these intentions for the day:

_____

_____

_____

_____

_____

Ask the Lord to bless these people today.

KEEP communicating with God today

Promptings from the Spirit   Blessings I received today

_____   _____

_____   _____

_____   _____

_____   _____

_____   _____

What does the Father ask of us? What do the scriptures say? Have faith, have hope, live like his Son, help others on their way. What does he ask? Live like his Son. CSB Pg34

My TALK with God today	**Day**	**Date**

☐ **Morning Prayer**	☐ **Evening Prayer**	**ASK IN FAITH**

Three Things I am **THANKFUL** for Today:
1.
2.
3.

What do I need forgiveness for?

Turn this over to the Lord. **LET** go and let God handle it

Ask God to help with this challenge today.

Prayer with action makes a difference. I set these intentions for the day:

_____

_____

_____

_____

_____

Ask the Lord to bless these people today.

KEEP communicating with God today

Promptings from the Spirit	**Blessings I received today**
_____	_____
_____	_____
_____	_____
_____	_____
_____	_____

When I say do your best, I mean your very best. You are capable of so much more.
Gordon B. Hinckley

My TALK with God today ➤ **Day** **Date**

☐ **Morning Prayer**	☐ **Evening Prayer**	**ASK IN FAITH**

Three Things I am THANKFUL for Today:

1.

2.

3.

I turn this over to the Lord. **LET** go and let God handle it

Prayer with action makes a difference. I set these intentions for the day:

_____

_____

_____

_____

_____

What do I need forgiveness for?

Ask God to help with this challenge today.

Ask the Lord to bless these people today..

KEEP communicating with God today

Promptings from the Spirit	**Blessings I received today**
_____	_____
_____	_____
_____	_____
_____	_____
_____	_____

When thou passest through the waters, I will be with thee; and through the rivers, they shall not overflow thee: when thou walkest through the fire, thou shalt not be burned; neither shall the flame kindle upon thee.
Isaiah 43:2

My TALK with God today	Day	Date

☐ Morning Prayer	☐ Evening Prayer

ASK IN FAITH

What do I need forgiveness for?

Three Things I am **THANKFUL** for Today:
1.
2.
3.

I turn this over to the Lord. **LET** go and let God handle it

Ask God to help with this challenge today.

Prayer with action makes a difference. I set these intentions for the day:

_____

_____

_____

_____

_____

Ask the Lord to bless these people today..

KEEP communicating with God today

Promptings from the Spirit	Blessings I received today
_____	_____
_____	_____
_____	_____
_____	_____
_____	_____

When upon life's billows you are tempest-tossed, When you are discouraged, thinking all is lost, Count your many blessings; name them one by one, And it will surprise you what the Lord has done.
Hymn 241

My TALK with God today   **Day**   **Date**

☐ Morning Prayer	☐ Evening Prayer

ASK IN FAITH

Three Things I am **THANKFUL** for Today:

1.

2.

3.

I turn this over to the Lord. **LET** go and let God handle it

What do I need forgiveness for?

Ask God to help with this challenge today.

Prayer with action makes a difference. I set these intentions for the day:

_____

_____

_____

_____

_____

Ask the Lord to bless these people today..

KEEP communicating with God today

Promptings from the Spirit	Blessings I received today
_____	_____
_____	_____
_____	_____
_____	_____
_____	_____

When we have hope in Christ, we come to know that as we need to make and keep sacred covenants, our fondest desires and dreams can be fulfilled through Him.
M Russell Ballard

My TALK with God today   Day   Date

☐ Morning Prayer	☐ Evening Prayer

ASK IN FAITH

Three Things I am **THANKFUL** for Today:

1.

2.

3.

What do I need forgiveness for?

I turn this over to the Lord. **LET** go and let God handle it

Ask God to help with this challenge today.

Prayer with action makes a difference. I set these intentions for the day:

_____

_____

_____

_____

_____

_____

Ask the Lord to bless these people today..

KEEP communicating with God today

Promptings from the Spirit   **Blessings I received today**

_____   _____

_____   _____

_____   _____

_____   _____

_____   _____

Where, when my aching grows, Where, when I languish, Where, in my need to know, where can I run? Where is the quiet hand to calm my anguish? Who, who can understand?
He, only One.
Hymn 129

My TALK with God today   **Day**   **Date**

☐ Morning Prayer	☐ Evening Prayer

ASK IN FAITH

Three Things I am **THANKFUL** for Today:

1.

2.

3.

I turn this over to the Lord. **LET** go and let God handle it

What do I need forgiveness for?

Ask God to help with this challenge today.

Prayer with action makes a difference. I set these intentions for the day:

_____

_____

_____

_____

_____

Ask the Lord to bless these people today..

KEEP communicating with God today

Promptings from the Spirit	Blessings I received today
_____	_____
_____	_____
_____	_____
_____	_____
_____	_____

Wherefore comfort yourselves together, and edify one another, even as also ye do.
1 Thessalonians 5:11

My TALK with God today | **Day** | **Date**

☐ **Morning Prayer** ☐ **Evening Prayer**

ASK IN FAITH

What do I need forgiveness for?

Three Things I am **THANKFUL** for Today:

1.

2.

3.

I turn this over to the Lord. **LET** go and let God handle it

Ask God to help with this challenge today.

Prayer with action makes a difference. I set these intentions for the day:

_____

_____

_____

_____

_____

Ask the Lord to bless these people today..

KEEP communicating with God today

Promptings from the Spirit | **Blessings I received today**

_____ | _____

_____ | _____

_____ | _____

_____ | _____

_____ | _____

Wherefore receive ye one another, as Christ also received us to the glory of God. Romans 15:7

My TALK with God today   **Day**   **Date**

☐   **Morning Prayer**   ☐   **Evening Prayer**

ASK IN FAITH

Three Things I am **THANKFUL** for Today:

1.

2.

3.

I turn this over to the Lord. **LET** go and let God handle it

What do I need forgiveness for?

Ask God to help with this challenge today.

Prayer with action makes a difference. I set these intentions for the day:

_____

_____

_____

_____

_____

Ask the Lord to bless these people today..

KEEP communicating with God today

Promptings from the Spirit   **Blessings I received today**

_____   _____

_____   _____

_____   _____

_____   _____

_____   _____

Wherefore, be of good cheer, and do not fear, for I the Lord am with you, and will stand by you.
D&C 68:6

My TALK with God today → **Day**   **Date**

☐ **Morning Prayer**	☐ **Evening Prayer**

ASK IN FAITH

Three Things I am **THANKFUL** for Today:

1.

2.

3.

I turn this over to the Lord. **LET** go and let God handle it

What do I need forgiveness for?

Prayer with action makes a difference. I set these intentions for the day:

_____

_____

_____

_____

_____

Ask God to help with this challenge today.

Ask the Lord to bless these people today..

KEEP communicating with God today

Promptings from the Spirit	**Blessings I received today**
_____	_____
_____	_____
_____	_____
_____	_____
_____	_____

Wherefore, fear not, little flock; do good; let earth and hell combine against you, for if ye are built upon my rock, they cannot prevail.
D&C 6:34

My TALK with God today	Day		Date

☐ Morning Prayer	☐ Evening Prayer

ASK IN FAITH

What do I need forgiveness for?

Three Things I am **THANKFUL** for Today:

1.

2.

3.

I turn this over to the Lord. **LET** go and let God handle it

Ask God to help with this challenge today.

Prayer with action makes a difference. I set these intentions for the day:

_____

_____

_____

_____

_____

Ask the Lord to bless these people today..

KEEP communicating with God today

Promptings from the Spirit	Blessings I received today
_____	_____
_____	_____
_____	_____
_____	_____
_____	_____

Wherefore, I say unto you, that ye ought to forgive one another; for he that forgiveth not his brother his trespasses standeth condemned before the Lord; for there remaineth in him the greater sin.
D&C 64:9

My TALK with God today → **Day**   **Date**

☐ **Morning Prayer**	☐ **Evening Prayer**

ASK IN FAITH

Three Things I am **THANKFUL** for Today:

1.

2.

3.

I turn this over to the Lord. **LET** go and let God handle it

What do I need forgiveness for?

Ask God to help with this challenge today.

Prayer with action makes a difference. I set these intentions for the day:

_____

_____

_____

_____

_____

Ask the Lord to bless these people today.

KEEP communicating with God today

Promptings from the Spirit   **Blessings I received today**

_____ _____

_____ _____

_____ _____

_____ _____

_____ _____

Wherefore, lift up thy heart and rejoice, and cleave unto the covenants which thou hast made.
D&C 25:13

My TALK with God today

Day _____ **Date** _____

☐ Morning Prayer	☐ Evening Prayer

ASK IN FAITH

Three Things I am **THANKFUL** for Today:

1.

2.

3.

I turn this over to the Lord. **LET** go and let God handle it

What do I need forgiveness for?

Prayer with action makes a difference. I set these intentions for the day:

_____

_____

_____

_____

_____

Ask God to help with this challenge today.

Ask the Lord to bless these people today.

KEEP communicating with God today

Promptings from the Spirit	Blessings I received today
_____	_____
_____	_____
_____	_____
_____	_____
_____	_____

Wherefore, ye must press forward with a steadfastness in Christ, having a perfect brightness of hope, and a love of God and of all men. Wherefore, if ye shall press forward, feasting upon the word of Christ, and endure to the end, behold, thus saith the Father: Ye shall have eternal life.
2 Nephi 31:20

My TALK with God today ➤ **Day** **Date**

☐ Morning Prayer	☐ Evening Prayer

ASK IN FAITH

Three Things I am **THANKFUL** for Today:
1.
2.
3.

What do I need forgiveness for?

I turn this over to the Lord. **LET** go and let God handle it

Ask God to help with this challenge today.

Prayer with action makes a difference. I set these intentions for the day:

_____

_____

_____

_____

_____

Ask the Lord to bless these people today.

KEEP communicating with God today

Promptings from the Spirit	Blessings I received today
_____	_____
_____	_____
_____	_____
_____	_____
_____	_____

While the Lord will magnify us in both subtle and dramatic ways, he can only guide our footsteps when we move our feet.
John Bytheway

My TALK with God today **Day** **Date**

☐ **Morning Prayer** ☐ **Evening Prayer**

ASK IN FAITH

Three Things I am **THANKFUL** for Today:

1.

2.

3.

What do I need forgiveness for?

I turn this over to the Lord. **LET** go and let God handle it

Ask God to help with this challenge today.

Prayer with action makes a difference. I set these intentions for the day:

_____

_____

_____

_____

_____

Ask the Lord to bless these people today.

KEEP communicating with God today

Promptings from the Spirit   **Blessings I received today**

_____   _____

_____   _____

_____   _____

_____   _____

_____   _____

Who am I to judge another When I walk imperfectly? In the quiet heart is hidden Sorrow that the eye can't see. Who am I to judge another? Lord, I would follow thee. Hymn 220

My TALK with God today ➤	Day	Date

☐ Morning Prayer	☐ Evening Prayer	ASK IN FAITH

Three Things I am **THANKFUL** for Today:	**What do I need forgiveness for?**

1.

2.

3.

I turn this over to the Lord. **LET** go and let God handle it

Ask God to help with this challenge today.

Prayer with action makes a difference. I set these intentions for the day:

_____

_____

_____   **Ask the Lord to bless these people today.**

_____

_____

KEEP communicating with God today

Promptings from the Spirit   **Blessings I received today**

_____ _____

_____ _____

_____ _____

_____ _____

_____ _____

Whoso believeth in God might with surety hope for a better world, yea, even a place at the right hand of God.
Ether 12:4

My TALK with God today

Day

Date

☐ **Morning Prayer** ☐ **Evening Prayer**

ASK IN FAITH

Three Things I am **THANKFUL** for Today:

1.

2.

3.

I turn this over to the Lord. **LET** go and let God handle it

What do I need forgiveness for?

Ask God to help with this challenge today.

Prayer with action makes a difference. I set these intentions for the day:

_____

_____

_____

_____

_____

Ask the Lord to bless these people today.

KEEP communicating with God today

Promptings from the Spirit

Blessings I received today

_____ _____

_____ _____

_____ _____

_____ _____

_____ _____

With all lowliness and meekness, with longsuffering, forbearing one another in love.
Ephesians 4:2

My TALK with God today   Day   Date

☐ Morning Prayer	☐ Evening Prayer

ASK IN FAITH

What do I need forgiveness for?

Three Things I am **THANKFUL** for Today:

1.

2.

3.

I turn this over to the Lord. **LET** go and let God handle it

Ask God to help with this challenge today.

Prayer with action makes a difference. I set these intentions for the day:

_____

_____

_____

_____

_____

Ask the Lord to bless these people today.

KEEP communicating with God today

Promptings from the Spirit	Blessings I received today
_____	_____
_____	_____
_____	_____
_____	_____
_____	_____

With God's help, good cheer permits us to rise above the depressing present or difficult circumstances. It is sunshine when clouds block the light.
Marvin J. Ashton

My TALK with God today | **Day** | **Date**

☐ **Morning Prayer** | ☐ **Evening Prayer** | **ASK IN FAITH**

Three Things I am **THANKFUL** for Today:

What do I need forgiveness for?

1.

2.

3.

I turn this over to the Lord. **LET** go and let God handle it

Ask God to help with this challenge today.

Prayer with action makes a difference. I set these intentions for the day:

_____

_____

_____

Ask the Lord to bless these people today.

_____

_____

KEEP communicating with God today

Promptings from the Spirit | **Blessings I received today**

_____ | _____

_____ | _____

_____ | _____

_____ | _____

_____ | _____

With His help and our faithfulness and endurance, we will prevail.
Dallin H. Oaks

My TALK with God today → **Day** | **Date**

| ☐ Morning Prayer | ☐ Evening Prayer | **ASK IN FAITH** |

What do I need forgiveness for?

Three Things I am **THANKFUL** for Today:

1.

2.

3.

I turn this over to the Lord. **LET** go and let God handle it

Ask God to help with this challenge today.

Prayer with action makes a difference. I set these intentions for the day:

_____

_____

_____

_____

Ask the Lord to bless these people today.

KEEP communicating with God today

Promptings from the Spirit   **Blessings I received today**

_____   _____

_____   _____

_____   _____

_____   _____

_____   _____

Ye shall walk in all the ways which the Lord your God hath commanded you, that ye may live, and that it may be well with you, and that ye may prolong your days in the land which ye shall possess. Deuteronomy 5:33

My TALK with God today → **Day** **Date**

☐ **Morning Prayer**   ☐ **Evening Prayer**

Three Things I am **THANKFUL** for Today:

1.

2.

3.

I turn this over to the Lord. **LET** go and let God handle it

What do I need forgiveness for?

Ask God to help with this challenge today.

Prayer with action makes a difference. I set these intentions for the day:

_____

_____

_____

_____

_____

Ask the Lord to bless these people today.

KEEP communicating with God today

Promptings from the Spirit   **Blessings I received today**

_____   _____

_____   _____

_____   _____

_____   _____

_____   _____

Yea, and are willing to mourn with those that mourn; yea, and comfort those that stand in need of comfort, and to stand as witnesses of God at all times and in all things, and in all places that ye may be in.
Mosiah 18:9

My TALK with God today → **Day**   **Date**

☐ Morning Prayer	☐ Evening Prayer

ASK IN FAITH

What do I need forgiveness for?

Three Things I am **THANKFUL** for Today:

1.

2.

3.

I turn this over to the Lord. **LET** go and let God handle it

Ask God to help with this challenge today.

Prayer with action makes a difference. I set these intentions for the day:

_____

_____

_____

_____

Ask the Lord to bless these people today.

KEEP communicating with God today

Promptings from the Spirit   **Blessings I received today**

_____   _____

_____   _____

_____   _____

_____   _____

_____   _____

Yea, and as often as my people repent will I forgive them their trespasses against me.
Mosiah 26:30

My TALK with God today → **Day**   **Date**

☐ **Morning Prayer**   ☐ **Evening Prayer**

Three Things I am **THANKFUL** for Today:
1.
2.
3.

I turn this over to the Lord. **LET** go and let God handle it

ASK IN FAITH

What do I need forgiveness for?

Ask God to help with this challenge today.

Prayer with action makes a difference. I set these intentions for the day:

_____

_____

_____

_____

_____

Ask the Lord to bless these people today.

KEEP communicating with God today

Promptings from the Spirit   **Blessings I received today**

_____   _____

_____   _____

_____   _____

_____   _____

_____   _____

Yea, behold, I will tell you in your mind and in your heart, by the Holy Ghost, which shall come upon you and which shall dwell in your heart.
D&C 8:2

My TALK with God today → Day

Date

☐ Morning Prayer	☐ Evening Prayer

ASK IN FAITH

Three Things I am **THANKFUL** for Today:
1.
2.
3.

I turn this over to the Lord. **LET** go and let God handle it

What do I need forgiveness for?

Ask God to help with this challenge today.

Prayer with action makes a difference. I set these intentions for the day:

_____

_____

_____

_____

_____

Ask the Lord to bless these people today.

KEEP communicating with God today

Promptings from the Spirit   **Blessings I received today**

_____   _____

_____   _____

_____   _____

_____   _____

_____   _____

Yet shall I be glorious in the eyes of the Lord, and my God shall be my strength.
1 Nephi 21:5